W9-BMH-439

MRCGP
MCQ PRACTICE PAPERS

PETER G ELLIOTT BSc MBChB MRCGP DRCOG

Examiner, Royal College of General Practitioners.
Course Organizer, Clwyd North Vocational Training Scheme.

PASTEST

First printed 1993

A catalogue record for this book is available from the British Library.

ISBN 0-906896-908

Text prepared by Turner Associates, Congleton, Cheshire.
Printed in Great Britain by The Cromwell Press, Wiltshire.

CONTENTS

INTRODUCTION

The membership examination of the Royal College of General Practitioners is a constantly changing animal and the MCQ component is no exception. The MCQ paper is worth 20% of the marks available in the exam as a whole. Over the last few years there have been a number of minor alterations to the structure and the content, however in 1992 big changes were made in three main areas.

Firstly, negative marking was abolished, this means that when doing these practice examinations there is no point in leaving a question blank when you do not know the answer. It pays to guess! Questions are scored on a basis of +1 mark for a correct answer and 0 for a wrong answer or a missed response.

Secondly, the emphasis has turned to items rather than questions. Instead of 60 questions numbered as such and each with 5 items, the current format is of 300 or more items and each stem has between 3 and 6 related items.

Thirdly, no new item is introduced without first being 'trialed' in an actual paper. This means that there will be more than 300 items to answer in the exam. In 1992 and 1993 it is 360, but it may well increase to 400 or more in the future. Only 300 items will actually count towards your final mark, the rest of the items are just being tested to see if they have good enough statistics to be included in a future examination. The problem is that the candidate does not know which ones these are, and has to answer all of them.

This book contains 5 practice papers each with 360 items and laid out in the same format as the Royal College of GP's examination. We have, however, added check boxes alongside each item to facilitate a system of self-assessment for those who wish to evaluate their knowledge upon completion of each practice paper. The balance of question topics is also the same as that currently used. The 60 additional items included in these papers are my best guess at the additional areas which the examiners will test in an examination.

The current balance between the 15 areas being tested is *approximately* as follows:

General Medicine	50 items
Psychiatry	30 items
Obstetrics and Gynaecology	30 items

Therapeutics	30 items
Paediatrics	25 items
Surgery	20 items
ENT	10 items
Dermatology	20 items
Ophthalmology	10 items
Legal/Ethical	10 items
Epidemiology/Research	10 items
Practice organisation	20 items
Care of the elderly	10 items
Physical Medicine/Trauma	15 items
Infectious Disease	10 items

Total: 300

I accept full responsibility for any mistakes which may have slipped through and for at times, rather simplistic explanations, but I have tried to reflect as accurately as possible the type and standard of questions that a candidate will encounter when he does the actual examination. I wish you good luck!

I would like to thank Freydis Campbell of PasTest for her help and encouragement, also Farine Clark of Pulse in which magazine some of these questions have appeared. Lastly I would like to thank my wife who has suffered many hours of me either sitting in front of a word processor or reading journals looking for questions.

P.E.
Clywd.

EXAM PREPARATION AND TECHNIQUE

In trying to pass any examination it helps to plan an effective revision programme that concentrates on the elements that are being examined and not the areas which the exam cannot or does not test.

There are certain basic principles which are relevant to each part of the MRCGP exam.

i) Read relevant literature.
    Remember that this is an examination of British general practice. You will gain far more from reading a book about the consultation than from reading about ENT or ophthalmology etc in a textbook.

ii) Ask yourself WHY?
    The exam asks you to appraise critically what you are doing. After every consultation ask yourself about the outcome: did you feel happy about it, do you think the patient was satisfied with your management? If not, why not, and how could you have managed the situation better. After every article you read, ask yourself why the article was written, whether it was relevant, what the main points were that the author was trying to get across, and were there better ways of achieving the same result. Be critical in a constructive way about your work and your reading.

iii) Form an alliance with other candidates.
    By meeting on a regular basis you can stimulate one another to be more critical. You can also divide the onerous task of ploughing through journals between the group and become very much more knowledgeable very quickly. Finally, by talking to colleagues you will retain more factual knowledge and also be able to clarify your ideas and opinions more clearly.

There are also specific techniques which will help you to prepare for the MCQ paper. It is often thought that you cannot improve your score in multiple choice examinations by repeatedly doing MCQs. I do not think that this is true. I think that candidates who do not improve their scores are using practice MCQs in the wrong way. What normally happens is that a candidate will spend a lot of time reading textbooks and then do a practice examination. It is far better to do an examination first, and then spend a lot of time reading around the answers and extending your knowledge in this way. Even with good teaching notes you still need to read around the topic.

There are only a limited number of areas relevant to general practice on which MCQs can be set and by doing a number of practice examinations in this way you can substantially increase your knowledge base and thus increase your overall score.

On Examination Day

By the time the day of the examination arrives you will certainly have invested a good deal of money, and probably a lot of time and effort in the exam. It is important that you do not blow it all on the day by making silly mistakes.

Again there are certain basic rules for approaching each part of the MRCGP.

i) Do not be tired.
    This may sound simple but if you have nights on call in the three to four days before the examination, then swop them. Try to keep your workload to a minimum. If you arrive tired you will not cope well with over 6 hours of written work.

ii) Arrive in time.
    Every year, for both the written and oral examinations, candidates underestimate the time it will take them to get to the examination venue. They arrive distressed and anxious and under these circumstances can never do themselves justice.

iii) Key into the task.
    By arriving in plenty of time, you have the chance to prepare mentally for the examination. Reading a current journal quietly just before going into the exam will start your brain thinking about general practice and current issues. When you sit down to start working on the papers you will already be in the right frame of mind and this will save you valuable time.

iv) Read the instructions.
    No matter how well you think you know the rules, always read the instructions at the beginning. There should be no changes from previous years but just in case there are, this is time well spent.

The majority of candidates will not be short of time in the MCQ paper, however there are a number of special techniques which should help:

i) Read the whole paper before you answer anything. This allows a lot of sub-conscious recall to happen before you start to mark your answers.

ii) Read every word in the stem and in each item. It is very easy to make simple mistakes by thinking that you read something that was not actually there.

iii) Mark the answer sheet carefully. Do not get the answer responses out of sequence. If you do have to alter a response rub it out well and mark the new response clearly. The answer sheets are marked by machine and an inadequately rubbed out answer could be intepreted as your true response.

iv) Answer every item. Remember there is NO negative marking and thus marks may be gained by guessing.

The Royal College of General Practitioners

SURNAME (Use block capitals)

INITIALS

INSTRUCTIONS	HOW TO MARK
✎ Use black lead pencil only (HB)	Not like these:
✎ Do NOT use ink or ballpoint pen	
✎ Make heavy black marks that fill the lozenge completely	But like this:
✎ Erase cleanly any answer you wish to change	
✎ Make no stray marks on this sheet	

ENTER CANDIDATE NUMBER HERE ☞

NOW SHOW THE NUMBER BY MARKING THE GRID ☞

☞ Each of the 360 items on the question paper is either true or false. If you believe that the answer is true, you should fill in the T lozenge; if you believe that it is false, fill in the F lozenge. Fill in the lozenge as shown above.

☞ Enter your answers to items 1 to 150 on this side; then turn over and continue entering your answers to items 151 to 360 on the other side.

Sample computer sheet, reproduced by kind permission of the Royal College of General Practitioners.

MCQ PRACTICE PAPER 1

360 Questions : time allowed 2 hours.

Indicate your answers clearly by putting a tick or cross in the box alongside each answer.

The following are true of hyperthyroidism:

- ☐ 1 the majority of cases are due to Graves' disease
- ☐ 2 toxic multinodular goitre is accompanied by raised TSH levels
- ☐ 3 block-replacement regimes are the treatment of choice for toxic adenomata
- ☐ 4 Graves' ophthalmopathy is more prevalent in smokers
- ☐ 5 postpartum thyroiditis typically has a thyrotoxic phase followed by a hypothyroid phase

A practice leaflet must include the following information in order to comply with the 1990 contract:

- ☐ 6 the age or date of birth of the doctors
- ☐ 7 the date of first registration of the practice nurse
- ☐ 8 the fees the practice charges for reports and certificates
- ☐ 9 whether the practice is computerised
- ☐ 10 the means by which disabled patients may gain access to the building

The following drugs are associated with sexual dysfunction:

- ☐ 11 clomipramine
- ☐ 12 propranolol
- ☐ 13 indomethacin
- ☐ 14 chlorpromazine
- ☐ 15 prednisolone

Concerning basal cell carcinoma:

- ☐ 16 it is the commonest skin malignancy
- ☐ 17 it occurs at sites of maximum skin exposure
- ☐ 18 it typically starts as a small ulcer
- ☐ 19 it crusting of the lesion indicates another diagnosis
- ☐ 20 it is commoner in those with freckles

1

A 45 year old male presents with a history of long term alcohol abuse, the following would be true if he had alcoholic cirrhosis:

- ☐ 21 absence of jaundice excludes the diagnosis
- ☐ 22 spider naevi are rare
- ☐ 23 pain over the liver is a frequent finding
- ☐ 24 testicular atrophy is common
- ☐ 25 prognosis is unaffected by cessation of alcohol once cirrhosis has developed

A patient presents at 32 weeks gestation with a primary attack of genital herpes, the following are true:

- ☐ 26 transplacental spread of the virus is rare
- ☐ 27 acyclovir orally has been shown to be teratogenic
- ☐ 28 if herpes lesions are present at the onset of labour, caesarian section is indicated
- ☐ 29 pregnant women are more resistant to herpes than non pregnant women
- ☐ 30 recurrent herpes carries the same risk to the fetus as a primary infection

Concerning Henoch Schönlein purpura:

- ☐ 31 there is typically a preceding upper respiratory tract infection
- ☐ 32 associated arthritis typically affects small joints of the hands and feet
- ☐ 33 arthritis lasts for an average of six weeks
- ☐ 34 haematuria occurs in the majority of cases
- ☐ 35 biopsy of skin lesions shows a characteristic appearance

The following treatments have been shown to be of benefit in the treatment of cyclical breast pain:

- ☐ 36 pyridoxine
- ☐ 37 diuretics
- ☐ 38 tamoxifen
- ☐ 39 gamolenic acid
- ☐ 40 hormone replacement therapy

A 23 year old patient presents with disturbed behaviour, the following are diagnostic of schizophrenia:

- ☐ 41 paranoid delusions
- ☐ 42 thoughts being inserted into the patients mind
- ☐ 43 voices in the third person commenting on the patients actions
- ☐ 44 visual hallucinations
- ☐ 45 ideas of reference

The following diseases are notifiable to the district community physician:

- ☐ 46 malaria
- ☐ 47 rubella
- ☐ 48 chicken pox
- ☐ 49 AIDS
- ☐ 50 mumps

The differential diagnosis of a single ulcer occurring in the mouth should include

- ☐ 51 aphthous ulcer
- ☐ 52 lichen planus
- ☐ 53 primary syphilis
- ☐ 54 agranulocytosis
- ☐ 55 Behçet's disease

Concerning Section 47 of the National Assistance Act:

- ☐ 56 it allows removal of a patient from his home for a maximum of three weeks
- ☐ 57 applications must be made to a magistrate
- ☐ 58 the applicant must be the patient's general practitioner
- ☐ 59 if admitted to hospital the patient may be treated without consent
- ☐ 60 the majority of those detained are below 65 years of age

A 14 year old girl presents with symptoms of an eating disorder, the following would support that diagnosis:

☐ 61 loss of pubic hair
☐ 62 primary amenorrhoea
☐ 63 raised LH levels
☐ 64 raised ESR
☐ 65 low cortisol levels

Concerning emergency contraception:

☐ 66 an intrauterine contraceptive device must be inserted within three days of coitus to be effective
☐ 67 insertion of an intrauterine contraceptive device has been shown to be more effective than hormonal methods
☐ 68 failed hormonal contraception is an indication for termination of pregnancy on the grounds of teratogenic risk
☐ 69 established breast feeding is a contraindication to hormonal postcoital contraception
☐ 70 surveys have shown that approximately 50% of women are unaware of postcoital methods of contraception

In bowel obstruction

☐ 71 colicky abdominal pain is characteristically the earliest symptom
☐ 72 passing flatus after the onset of pain casts doubt on the diagnosis
☐ 73 if the site of obstruction is in the distal large bowel, vomiting is a late feature
☐ 74 visible peristalsis is diagnostic of obstruction
☐ 75 bowel sounds are typically described as borborygmi

A child attends for the third time with a five week history of cough without malaise which has not responded to symptomatic remedies:

- ☐ 76 chest X-ray is mandatory
- ☐ 77 a trial of bronchodilators is indicated
- ☐ 78 this is a typical presentation of pertussis
- ☐ 79 inhaled foreign bodies present in this way
- ☐ 80 a trial of antibiotics is indicated

Concerning osteoarthritis

- ☐ 81 it shows a familial tendency
- ☐ 82 it is more common in overweight people
- ☐ 83 the picture of radiological damage correlates closely with the clinical condition
- ☐ 84 if a diagnosis of early osteoarthritis is made, joint exercise should be severely restricted
- ☐ 85 it is commonest in the hips

A 45 year old man presents with hearing loss, the following would support a diagnosis of it being noise induced:

- ☐ 86 a conductive deafness
- ☐ 87 predominantly low frequency loss
- ☐ 88 recruitment
- ☐ 89 no response to a hearing aid
- ☐ 90 acute onset of hearing loss in one ear

Your practice has a high proportion of shiftworkers, research has shown that

- ☐ 91 the majority of shiftworkers dislike nightwork
- ☐ 92 they have an increased incidence of industrial accidents
- ☐ 93 they have an increased cardiovascular mortality
- ☐ 94 they have an increased incidence of peptic ulceration
- ☐ 95 there is an increase in feelings of paranoia

Concerning solvent abuse:

- ☐ 96 it is typically an activity of males rather than females
- ☐ 97 deaths are associated with the presence of aerosol propellants (freons)
- ☐ 98 persistent cerebellar signs are suggestive of prolonged use
- ☐ 99 the majority of abusers will stop within six months of starting the habit
- ☐ 100 the occurrence of visual hallucinations would suggest other psychopathology

The following are true of primary nocturnal enuresis in childhood:

- ☐ 101 the majority of children are dry throughout the night by the age of three
- ☐ 102 if associated with daytime wetting is more likely to be associated with organic disease
- ☐ 103 pad and buzzer alarms become a more effective treatment in the child who is wet after the age of ten years
- ☐ 104 persistence into adult life occurs in less than 1% of patients
- ☐ 105 repeatedly lifting a child during the night has been shown to be as effective as drug therapy

The following items are available on an F.P.10:

- ☐ 106 pen insulin injection devices
- ☐ 107 click count syringes for the visually impaired
- ☐ 108 finger pricking devices
- ☐ 109 glucose tablets
- ☐ 110 blood pricking lancets

Withdrawal of corticosteroids is typically associated with

- ☐ 111 conjunctivitis
- ☐ 112 hypertension
- ☐ 113 loss of weight
- ☐ 114 arthritis
- ☐ 115 painful itchy skin nodules

A higher rate night visit fee is paid for the following:

- ☐ 116 you have a rota with another single handed general practitioner and he performs a visit on your patient
- ☐ 117 if a visit is received at 07.45 and made at 08.05
- ☐ 118 a patient telephones you at 07.00 and you meet them at your surgery at 07.55
- ☐ 119 your local community hospital calls you to see one of your patients in the casualty department at 03.00
- ☐ 120 a patient calls you to attend a threatened miscarriage at 01.00

Epidemiology of chronic bronchitis

- ☐ 121 Northern Ireland has the highest mortality rate for chronic bronchitis in the world
- ☐ 122 more than 15% of males between 40-60 years have been shown to have evidence of chronic bronchitis
- ☐ 123 chronic bronchitis accounts for more lost time from work than any other illness
- ☐ 124 the disease is more prevalent in urban than rural areas

Concerning tinnitus:

- ☐ 125 it is typically associated with conductive deafness
- ☐ 126 it is associated with gout
- ☐ 127 it has been shown to be due to a carotid bruit in some cases
- ☐ 128 treatment of associated depression is rarely helpful
- ☐ 129 cochlear nerve section is associated with a worsening of the noise

When considering gastric and duodenal ulceration

- ☐ 130 night pain is more common with duodenal ulcers
- ☐ 131 a gastric ulcer is more likely to bleed
- ☐ 132 *Heliobacter pylori* is found in over 90% of patients with duodenal ulcer
- ☐ 133 a positive family history is common for both sites
- ☐ 134 a recent survey has shown that of patients over 40 years of age presenting with dyspepsia for the first time the majority will have a malignancy

Carcinoma of the bladder

- ☐ 135 typically presents with haematuria
- ☐ 136 the incidence is increasing in women
- ☐ 137 is associated with cigarette smoking
- ☐ 138 if superficial, the majority will not recur within 5 years if treated by cystodiathermy
- ☐ 139 is associated with previous abuse of alcohol

The following features would suggest a cerebral infarct rather than a cerebral haemorrhage:

- ☐ 140 bilateral extensor plantar responses
- ☐ 141 a previous transient ischaemic attack
- ☐ 142 co-existing cardiac disease
- ☐ 143 consciousness impaired 24 hours after the onset of the event
- ☐ 144 abrupt onset accompanied by vomiting

The following are at an increased risk of chronic open angled glaucoma:

- ☐ 145 extremely long sighted patients
- ☐ 146 diabetics
- ☐ 147 relatives of patients with glaucoma
- ☐ 148 patients over 65 years of age
- ☐ 149 those with astigmatism

An unexplained finding of thrombocytopenia on a routine full blood count would be explained by

- ☐ 150 inadequate mixing of the sample
- ☐ 151 polyarteritis nodosa
- ☐ 152 systemic lupus erythematosis
- ☐ 153 intercurrent viral infection
- ☐ 154 treatment with dipyrimadole

The following are risk factors for increased mortality in an elderly patient with a chest infection:

☐ 155 co-existing atrial fibrillation
☐ 156 a very low white cell count
☐ 157 hypotension
☐ 158 recent influenza vaccine
☐ 159 confusion

The following statements have been shown to be true of lipid lowering drugs:

☐ 160 cholestyramine is allowed in pregnancy and breast feeding
☐ 161 simvastatin is associated with sleep disturbance
☐ 162 the flushing induced by nicotinic acid is typically improved by low dose aspirin
☐ 163 regular monitoring of liver function tests is necessary on treatment with bezafibrate
☐ 164 none of the available agents is licensed for use in children

General practitioners

☐ 165 are responsible for any errors made by their practice nurse
☐ 166 are responsible for care of their patients at all times
☐ 167 are obliged to order any drug (that does not appear on the black list) for the treatment of a patient on an NHS prescription form
☐ 168 are responsible for errors made by a spouse when answering the telephone
☐ 169 if complaints are made against them the most probable reason is failure to refer to hospital

A 25 year old patient presents with a history of heavy periods:

☐ 170 approximately half the patients who complain of heavy periods have a measurably normal menstrual loss
☐ 171 dysfunctional uterine bleeding is usually caused by fibroids
☐ 172 mefenamic acid reduces bleeding by an average of 25%
☐ 173 dilatation and curettage is indicated in all patients
☐ 174 endometrial ablation can be performed using laser treatment

The following may be associated with a diagnosis of retinal detachment:

- ☐ 175 myopia
- ☐ 176 previous cataract surgery
- ☐ 177 normal distance vision
- ☐ 178 black spots in front of the eyes
- ☐ 179 co-existing diabetic retinopathy

Subarachnoid haemorrhage in the over 65 year olds

- ☐ 180 only accounts for approximately 5% of all cases
- ☐ 181 is typically due to a ruptured atherosclerotic blood vessel
- ☐ 182 characteristically presents with headache
- ☐ 183 has a decreased mortality in comparison to younger patients
- ☐ 184 has a worse prognosis in hypertensive patients

The following drugs have been shown to decrease mortality following a myocardial infarction:

- ☐ 185 captopril
- ☐ 186 timolol
- ☐ 187 isosorbide mononitrate
- ☐ 188 nifedipine
- ☐ 189 streptokinase

A patient visiting this country from Australia is involved in a road traffic accident. Immediate and follow up care is necessary. Which of the following statements are true:

- ☐ 190 immediate and necessary care is provided by the NHS free of charge
- ☐ 191 all follow up care is private
- ☐ 192 all prescriptions issued must be private
- ☐ 193 domiciliary nursing is provided on the same basis as to UK residents
- ☐ 194 a fee can be charged for attending the patient at the road traffic accident

Constitutional delay in puberty is associated with the following:

- ☐ 195 boys are more often affected than girls
- ☐ 196 bone age on X-ray examination corresponds to chronological age
- ☐ 197 gonadotrophins are typically raised
- ☐ 198 a family history of delayed puberty or menarche

When considering breast feeding

- ☐ 199 the duration of early feeds should be limited
- ☐ 200 both breasts must be used at each feed
- ☐ 201 poor positioning of the baby is the commonest cause of nipple pain
- ☐ 202 terminating feeding prematurely from one breast will decrease the nutritional value of the feed
- ☐ 203 late onset sore nipples are typically due to thrush
- ☐ 204 breast feeding is associated with an increase in the incidence of breast cancer in later life

When considering statistical bias in a scientific paper:

- ☐ 205 retrospective studies are generally more open to bias than prospective studies
- ☐ 206 subjective results are more prone to bias than objective studies
- ☐ 207 standardisation decreases bias
- ☐ 208 stratified sampling causes more bias than random sampling
- ☐ 209 control groups are essential to decrease bias
- ☐ 210 random numbers are preferable to regular samples

The following factors would suggest an increased risk of suicide in depressed patients:

- ☐ 211 co-existing problems of alcohol abuse
- ☐ 212 history of aggressive behaviour
- ☐ 213 co-existing chronic physical illness
- ☐ 214 living in a rural environment
- ☐ 215 married status

An adult patient who is otherwise well complains of hair loss all over the scalp. The following are possible causes:

☐ 216 iron deficiency
☐ 217 scalp ringworm
☐ 218 anti-coagulant therapy
☐ 219 alopecia areata
☐ 220 trichotillomania

Concerning ectopic pregnancy

☐ 221 the frequency is increasing in the UK
☐ 222 ectopic pregnancies secrete lower levels of HCG (human chorionic gonadotrophin) than a corresponding uterine gestation
☐ 223 ultrasound alone is diagnostic in the majority of cases
☐ 224 there is a positive association with the presence of an IUCD in the uterine cavity
☐ 225 the death rate is increasing in the UK

When treating an uncomplicated urinary tract infection in a pregnant patient the following drugs are considered to be free from any adverse affect on the pregnancy:

☐ 226 trimethoprim
☐ 227 nitrofurantoin
☐ 228 amoxycillin
☐ 229 ciprofloxacin
☐ 230 cephalexin

Pompholyx

☐ 231 is a contact dermatitis
☐ 232 characteristically occurs on the soles of the feet and the palms of the hands
☐ 233 is unresponsive to topical steroids
☐ 234 is associated with atopic conditions
☐ 235 is typically itchy

When considering ovarian cancer

☐ 236 it is commoner in multiparous women
☐ 237 there is an increased incidence if a first degree relative has had the disease
☐ 238 the overall 5 year survival is greater than 50%
☐ 239 the majority of patients present with abnormal vaginal bleeding
☐ 240 protection afforded by the combined oral contraceptive is proportional to the duration of usage

Cognitive behaviour therapy

☐ 241 concentrates on negative patterns of thinking
☐ 242 is suitable for marital and sexual problems
☐ 243 is of benefit in eating disorders
☐ 244 patients who abuse substances have been shown to benefit
☐ 245 chronic pain is unresponsive to treatment by this method

Plasma monitoring has been shown to be of value in the treatment of epilepsy with the following drugs:

☐ 246 primidone
☐ 247 ethosuximide
☐ 248 sodium valproate
☐ 249 vigabactrin
☐ 250 clonazepam

Faecal occult blood testing

☐ 251 fulfils Wilson's criteria for a screening test
☐ 252 in screening programmes the majority of positive stool samples are false positives
☐ 253 with a three day test the sensitivity for colonic carcinoma is over 90%
☐ 254 the test is more sensitive for caecal tumours than for sigmoid tumours
☐ 255 banana ingestion has been shown to cause false positives

In diabetic retinopathy

- ☐ 256 it typically starts in the peripheral retina
- ☐ 257 it is the commonest cause of blindness in those under 65 years of age
- ☐ 258 it typically responds to laser treatment
- ☐ 259 micro-aneurysms are a feature of background retinopathy
- ☐ 260 new vessel formation can occur on the conjunctiva

A one year old boy presents with an episode of unconsciousness during an episode of crying. The following would support a diagnosis of breath holding attack:

- ☐ 261 recovery within one minute
- ☐ 262 upturned eyes during the attack
- ☐ 263 drowsiness after the attack
- ☐ 264 extended tonic posture during the attack
- ☐ 265 cyanosis

Prolapsed intervertebral discs are associated with

- ☐ 266 a positive femoral stretch test with an L4-L5 lesion
- ☐ 267 pain is felt in the muscles innervated by the damaged nerve root
- ☐ 268 an L2-L3 lesion may be accompanied by an extensor plantar response
- ☐ 269 loss of bladder function
- ☐ 270 loss of ankle reflex if L5-S1 root is compressed

In pseudomembranous colitis

- ☐ 271 it is typically associated with previous antibiotic therapy
- ☐ 272 *Yersinia* is the most commonly isolated organism
- ☐ 273 treatment with metronidazole has been shown to be effective
- ☐ 274 the passing of fresh blood in the stools is a characteristic feature
- ☐ 275 it is associated with an eosinophilia in the peripheral blood film

A patient with Alzheimers' disease is recognised to have the following signs and symptoms:

- ☐ 276 a preference for routine
- ☐ 277 a loss of long term memory
- ☐ 278 a loss of speech in the later stages
- ☐ 279 spatial disorientation
- ☐ 280 ataxia

In the management of non insulin dependent diabetes mellitus

- ☐ 281 metformin is associated with weight gain
- ☐ 282 sulphonylureas become less effective with time
- ☐ 283 tight blood sugar control is the goal of treatment in the elderly
- ☐ 284 the majority of newly diagnosed patients will show clinical evidence of retinopathy
- ☐ 285 the diet for overweight patients should contain approximately half the total calories as carbohydrate

A three year old child presents with rhinitis, sneezing and conjunctivitis typical of hay fever. The following treatments are approved for use in this age group:

- ☐ 286 ipatropium bromide nasal spray (Rinatec)
- ☐ 287 xylometazoline nasal drops
- ☐ 288 terfenadine suspension (Triludan)
- ☐ 289 azelastine nasal spray (Rhinolast)
- ☐ 290 sodium cromoglycate eye drops (Opticrom)

When investigating a patient for ischaemic heart disease

- ☐ 291 ST segment changes on a resting ECG indicate myocardial ischaemia
- ☐ 292 on exercise testing the degree of ST depression at a given workload is of diagnostic relevance
- ☐ 293 exercise testing associated with a fall in blood pressure is of good prognostic significance
- ☐ 294 24 h ambulatory monitoring shows a ratio of painless to painful ischaemia of 4:1
- ☐ 295 coronary angiography has significant morbidity in 5% of patients

Dupuytren's contracture

- [ ] 296 is typically painful
- [ ] 297 the ring finger is the most commonly affected digit
- [ ] 298 is associated with epilepsy
- [ ] 299 is typically seen in white men
- [ ] 300 is characteristically unilateral

The following have been shown to respond to placebos in clinical trials:

- [ ] 301 hyperlipidaemia
- [ ] 302 hay fever
- [ ] 303 blood glucose levels
- [ ] 304 blood pressure levels
- [ ] 305 post operative pain

The following are true of heartsink patients:

- [ ] 306 the majority are women
- [ ] 307 they typically present with a single problem
- [ ] 308 they have higher referral rates than the average population
- [ ] 309 the average general practitioner is able to identify more than 50 such patients on his list
- [ ] 310 they have significantly more social problems than the average population

When considering a diagnosis of phimosis in childhood

- [ ] 311 by 6 months of age approximately 50% of boys have a retractable foreskin
- [ ] 312 circumcision is associated with a higher complication rate than other childhood operative procedures
- [ ] 313 the inability to clean under the foreskin is associated with the development of cancer of the penis in adulthood
- [ ] 314 if untreated has been shown to lead to problems with sexual function in later life

Studies have shown that people in social class 5 have an increased incidence of the following conditions when compared with those in social class 1:

- ☐ 315 motor vehicle accidents
- ☐ 316 pneumonia
- ☐ 317 lung cancer

Glue ear is associated with

- ☐ 318 a peak incidence at approximately 7 years of age
- ☐ 319 an increased incidence of tympanosclerosis after grommet insertion
- ☐ 320 an increased incidence in winter and spring
- ☐ 321 an increased incidence in the children of smokers
- ☐ 322 spontaneous resolution within 12 months in over 90% of children

Sickle cell disease is associated with

- ☐ 323 priapism
- ☐ 324 impaired fertility in women
- ☐ 325 an increased incidence of stroke
- ☐ 326 gall stones in the majority of patients
- ☐ 327 an enlarged spleen after the first decade of life

Psoriatic arthropathy is associated with the following features:

- ☐ 328 a preceding history of skin lesions in the majority of patients
- ☐ 329 non-involvement of the distal interphalangeal joints
- ☐ 330 subcutaneous nodules
- ☐ 331 the presence of eye lesions in the majority of patients
- ☐ 332 the development of some evidence of joint involvement in the majority of patients with psoriasis

The following statements are true about jaundiced patients:

- ☐ 333 non A – non B hepatitis can be transmitted by drinking contaminated water
- ☐ 334 hepatitis B is associated with the development of hepatocellular carcinoma
- ☐ 335 acute cholangitis carries a mortality rate of about 40%
- ☐ 336 hepatitis A typically produces a carrier state following the acute infection

An 80 year old male patient has been complaining of feeling tired all the time and you have found no abnormality on examination. Following a range of investigations you can safely conclude that the following results are purely due to the effects of ageing:

- ☐ 337 a serum sodium of 125 mmol/l
- ☐ 338 a serum urea of 9.5 mmol/l
- ☐ 339 a serum bilirubin of 22 mmol/l
- ☐ 340 a serum calcium of 2.0 mmol/l
- ☐ 341 a drop of 30 mm Hg in systolic blood pressure on standing

The following are true about the epidemiology of AIDS:

- ☐ 342 the UK has the highest incidence in Europe
- ☐ 343 in the USA, AIDS is one of the top five causes of death
- ☐ 344 approximately 10 million people world wide are HIV positive
- ☐ 345 20% of UK AIDS cases are intravenous drug addicts
- ☐ 346 over 50% of HIV positive patients in Scotland are intravenous drug abusers

When considering symptoms due to a carcinoma of the colon at the time of presentation

- ☐ 347 pain occurs in the majority of patients with a right sided lesion
- ☐ 348 a palpable mass is present in the majority of those with a lesion in the left colon
- ☐ 349 change in bowel habit is present with the majority of rectal lesions
- ☐ 350 the majority of right sided lesions bleed
- ☐ 351 the majority of rectal lesions bleed

Dithranol

- ☐ 352 is indicated for rapidly spreading psoriatic lesions
- ☐ 353 in prolonged usage is associated with an increase in the incidence of skin malignancies
- ☐ 354 'short contact' therapy has been shown to be less effective than conventional treatment
- ☐ 355 is contra-indicated if potent steroids have been used in the previous 14 days

Febrile convulsions

- ☐ 356 have a prevalence of between 2-5%
- ☐ 357 are typically associated with fevers due to bacterial infections
- ☐ 358 post ictally are typically associated with transient neurological deficits
- ☐ 359 in a 3 year old child who fails to respond to 5 mg rectal diazepam. The dose cannot be repeated for one hour
- ☐ 360 have a stronger family history than idiopathic epilepsy

MCQ PRACTICE PAPER 2

360 Questions : time allowed 2 hours.

In Terminal Care

- ☐ 1 the majority of people die at home
- ☐ 2 the majority of patients with pain have more than one type of pain
- ☐ 3 over 90% of patient pain can be controlled with drugs
- ☑ 4 with severe pain, intramuscular analgesics are more effective than the equivalent dose administered by the oral route
- ☐ 5 portable syringe devices need to have the syringe changed at approximately six hour intervals

Babies who are small for their gestational age are at risk of the following:

- ☐ 6 intraventricular haemorrhage
- ☐ 7 convulsions in later life
- ☐ 8 remaining small
- ☐ 9 learning difficulties
- ☐ 10 diabetes in later life

Korsakov's syndrome is associated with

- ☐ 11 denial of amnesia
- ☐ 12 obsession with time
- ☑ 13 confabulation
- ☑ 14 ritualistic behaviour
- ☐ 15 echopraxia

Viral pneumonia has been shown to be a consequence of infections with the following:

- ☑ 16 measles
- ☑ 17 mumps
- ☑ 18 varicella
- ☐ 19 rubella
- ☑ 20 cytomegalovirus

In Bell's palsy

- ☐ 21 the majority of patients will make a recovery within three weeks
- ☐ 22 brain stem lesions will cause loss of taste
- ☐ 23 oral steroids have been shown to be effective
- ☐ 24 lacrimation is unaffected
- ☐ 25 repeat attacks resolve more readily than the initial attack

Concerning episiotomy:

- ☐ 26 studies have shown that a wait of one hour for stitching is associated with significant infection
- ☐ 27 episiotomy has been shown to prevent development of rectocele
- ☐ 28 episiotomy rates are higher for home confinements
- ☐ 29 tearing of the perineum does not occur once episiotomy has been performed
- ☐ 30 Apgar scores of babies born to mothers who have had an episiotomy have been shown to be higher than those without

In differentiating between migraine and tension headache, the following would support a diagnosis of the latter:

- ☐ 31 a hatband distribution of pain
- ☐ 32 tender spots on the scalp during the headache
- ☐ 33 flushing at the onset of the headache
- ☐ 34 a watery eye during the period of the headache
- ☐ 35 facial pain occuring during an attack of headache

Infantile pyloric stenosis

- ☐ 36 shows an increased familial incidence
- ☐ 37 typically presents between 2-3 months of age
- ☐ 38 babies tend to become acidotic
- ☐ 39 is commoner in males
- ☐ 40 blood in the vomit would indicate other pathology

Population studies have shown that disability in old age can be reduced by

☐ 41 lowering the average diastolic blood pressure by 10 mm Hg
☐ 42 30 minutes walking daily
☐ 43 two servings of oily fish per week
☐ 44 decreasing the average calcium intake
☐ 45 decreasing the average sodium intake

Acute pancreatitis is associated with

☐ 46 gall stones
☐ 47 raised cholesterol levels
☐ 48 mumps infection
☐ 49 first attacks that are less severe than subsequent episodes
☐ 50 hypocalcaemia

Concerning warts:

☐ 51 the majority of patients with warts develop immunity within 2 years
☐ 52 salicylic acid preparations should be applied for 3 months or more
☐ 53 topical podophyllin must be left on the wart without washing for 24 hours
☐ 54 cryotherapy with liquid nitrogen typically scars
☐ 55 podophyllin is teratogenic

You are consulted by the parents of an apparently healthy child who refuses to sleep at night. The following are true:

☐ 56 at 3 months the average child has approximately 4 episodes of nocturnal wakefulness
☐ 57 at 6 months the majority of children have 15 hours of sleep during the night
☐ 58 a regular night time routine has been shown to solve the majority of sleep problems
☐ 59 children with persistent sleep disturbance have an increased incidence of other behavioral problems
☐ 60 a child who persistently cries at night should be left no longer than 5 minutes

The following drugs used in the treatment of rheumatoid arthritis have the side effects stated:

- ☐ 61 gold injections cause exfoliative dermatitis
- ☐ 62 penicillamine is associated with azoospermia
- ☐ 63 methotrexate has been implicated in hepatic fibrosis
- ☐ 64 sulphasalazin is associated with thrombocytopenia
- ☐ 65 chloroquine produces retinal damage

The following are true of hand, foot and mouth disease:

- ☐ 66 a sore throat is characteristic
- ☐ 67 typically the spots are itchy
- ☐ 68 spots appearing on the buttocks would exclude the diagnosis
- ☐ 69 it has an incubation period of approximately 21 days
- ☐ 70 it typically responds to oral penicillin

The majority of patients with Down's syndrome will

- ☐ 71 have an IQ of between 20 and 50
- ☐ 72 die before they reach 50 years of age
- ☐ 73 have a congenital heart disorder
- ☐ 74 have a behaviour disorder
- ☐ 75 develop hypothyroidism

A 30 year old man presents with a knee effusion following a recent episode of urethral discharge. The following would support a diagnosis of Reiter's disease:

- ☐ 76 clear synovial fluid on aspiration
- ☐ 77 an ESR of 60 mm/h
- ☐ 78 stomatitis
- ☐ 79 lesions on the soles of the feet
- ☐ 80 conjuctivitis

Motor neurone disease is typically associated with

- ☐ 81 symptoms of dementia
- ☐ 82 painful muscle cramps in the early stages of the disease
- ☐ 83 a symmetrical distribution of weakness and wasting
- ☐ 84 a survival of more than 5 years from the time of onset
- ☐ 85 the preservation of sphincter function

In sub-arachnoid haemorrhage

- ☐ 86 the majority of patients will die without warning
- ☐ 87 the peak age range is in the under 35 year olds
- ☐ 88 there is a familial tendency
- ☐ 89 the majority of patients who have surgery achieve their previous quality of life
- ☐ 90 the risk of epilepsy is increased following a haemorrhage

The following are associated with the second trimester of pregnancy:

- ☐ 91 a cardiac output which is about 40% above the non pregnant state
- ☐ 92 enhanced absorption of dietary iron
- ☐ 93 increased gastric acid secretion
- ☐ 94 delay in gastric emptying
- ☐ 95 increased introversion

The following drugs have been shown to potentiate the effects of alcohol:

- ☐ 96 phenytoin
- ☐ 97 indomethacin
- ☐ 98 atenolol
- ☐ 99 chlorpheniramine
- ☐ 100 monoamine oxidase inhibitors

Laser is used for the treatment of the following ophthalmological conditions:

- ☐ 101 amaurosis fugax
- ☐ 102 acute glaucoma
- ☐ 103 senile macular degeneration
- ☐ 104 diabetic background retinopathy
- ☐ 105 myopia

Puerperal depressive illness

- ☐ 106 has been shown to occur in 10% of pregnancies
- ☐ 107 is commoner in single parents
- ☐ 108 is associated with lack of 'bonding'
- ☐ 109 is associated with a previous psychiatric history
- ☐ 110 has been shown to be associated with a decreased level of progestogen six weeks post delivery

In carcinoma of the cervix

- ☐ 111 it has an association with human papilloma virus infection
- ☐ 112 the majority of patients survive more than five years
- ☐ 113 smoking has been shown to increase the risks of contracting the disease
- ☐ 114 cytology has been shown to be reliable in identifying frank carcinoma
- ☐ 115 the peak incidence occurs between 40-55 years of age

Concerning hypoglycaemia

- ☐ 116 it is defined as a blood glucose level of less than 2.2 mmol/l
- ☐ 117 catecholamines decrease blood glucose concentrations
- ☐ 118 alcohol potentiates the effects of insulin
- ☐ 119 strict control of diabetes makes patients less sensitive to falls in blood glucose levels
- ☐ 120 the face typically flushes at the onset of a hypoglycaemic episode

When looking at lesions on the ear the following should be considered:

- ☐ 121 basal cell carcinoma typically appears on the helix
- ☐ 122 tophi appear on the earlobe
- ☐ 123 chilblains of the ear never itch
- ☐ 124 psoriasis typically occurs all over the ear
- ☐ 125 kerato-acanthoma do not appear on the ear

Pulmonary fibrosis may result following administration of the drugs named below:

- ☐ 126 methotrexate
- ☐ 127 erythromycin
- ☐ 128 nitrofurantoin
- ☐ 129 amiodarone
- ☐ 130 busulphan

When considering flat feet (pes planus)

- ☐ 131 symptoms fail to correlate with the degree of structural alteration
- ☐ 132 the majority of children age 2 years have the condition
- ☐ 133 painful mobile flat feet are an indication for corrective surgery
- ☐ 134 they are typically associated with painful night cramps
- ☐ 135 if familial typically respond to corrective measures

The following expenses are directly reimbursed by the FHSA:

- ☐ 136 rent on premises
- ☐ 137 repairs to premises
- ☐ 138 lighting and heating costs
- ☐ 139 dressings and drugs for use in the surgery
- ☐ 140 insurance premiums on the surgery premises

Polymyalgia rheumatica and temporal arteritis are related in the following respects:

☐ 141 the age/sex distribution is the same
☐ 142 Asians are more often affected
☐ 143 myalgia is a typical feature
☐ 144 biopsy findings are identical
☐ 145 typical changes in the plasma electrophoretic pattern

The following statements are true of eardrums with a central perforation:

☐ 146 they typically produce a mucoid discharge
☐ 147 they are associated with the production of cholesteatoma
☐ 148 repair is possible via a tympanoplasty
☐ 149 urgent referral to an ENT surgeon is indicated

Dyspepsia treatments are noted for the following side effects:

☐ 150 aluminium salts cause diarrhoea
☐ 151 cisapride is typically associated with acute dyskinesia in young adults
☐ 152 misoprostol is associated with intermenstrual bleeding
☐ 153 metoclopramide is associated with elevated prolactin levels
☐ 154 H_2 receptor antagonists are associated with confusion in the elderly
☐ 155 omeprazole is associated with photosensitivity reactions

Avascular necrosis of the femoral head

☐ 156 is associated with slipped upper femoral epiphysis
☐ 157 is an occupational hazard of deep sea divers
☐ 158 is improved by the use of non steroidal anti-inflammatory drugs
☐ 159 pain is typically of sudden onset
☐ 160 X-ray changes are apparent at an early stage

Amiodarone in the treatment of ventricular arrhythmias is

- ☐ 161   contraindicated in the presence of impaired left ventricular function
- ☐ 162   associated with the presence of corneal deposits
- ☐ 163   associated with biochemical abnormalities of the thyroid
- ☐ 164   associated with skin sensitivity that is resistant to treatment with sunblock creams
- ☐ 165   associated with a dose related incidence of side effects

When advising patients about to undergo air travel a GP should be aware of the following facts:

- ☐ 166   people with a vital capacity less than 50% of the mean predicted for them, should not fly
- ☐ 167   there is no increase in fit frequency of epileptics
- ☐ 168   diabetics on oral hypoglycaemic agents will need to decrease their dosage if undertaking a prolonged eastbound flight
- ☐ 169   motion sickness on aircraft shows a tendency to increase with age
- ☐ 170   recent eye surgery is a contraindication to flying

Concerning indicative prescribing budgets:

- ☐ 171   they are only allocated to fund holding practices
- ☐ 172   if a practice underspends its budget, amounts saved can be added to future years budgets
- ☐ 173   practice formularies are compulsory
- ☐ 174   if a practice overspends, its budget remuneration can be witheld by the FHSA
- ☐ 175   patients on 'expensive' medication are not included in the budget

The following would support a diagnosis of irritable bowel syndrome:

- ☐ 176   nocturnal diarrhoea
- ☐ 177   absence of pain
- ☐ 178   associated menstrual disturbance
- ☐ 179   abdominal pain worsening on defaecation
- ☐ 180   onset associated with a proven gastro-intestinal infection

Your practice is reviewing its protocol for antenatal care. Research has shown that

☐ 181   routine ultrasound reduces the incidence of induction for alleged postmaturity

☐ 182   anti-smoking education reduces the incidence of low birth weight babies

☐ 183   measuring fundal heights routinely decreases perinatal mortality

☐ 184   routine antenatal care detects the majority of small for gestational age babies

☐ 185   routine kick charts have been shown to reduce the chances of perinatal death

Concerning breast lumps:

☐ 186   cysts are more prevalent in post menopausal women

☐ 187   cysts should not be aspirated by general practitioners

☐ 188   the majority of solitary breast cysts will recur within 2 years of initial aspiration

☐ 189   patients with breast cysts have an increased risk of developing breast cancer

☐ 190   lumpy breasts which are cyclically painful have been shown to respond to oil of evening primrose

The following patients are not charged for an eye examination:

☐ 191   diabetics

☐ 192   those on income support

☐ 193   pregnant women

☐ 194   people over 65 years of age

☐ 195   those with a parent with glaucoma

Under the terms of service of a general practitioners contract, he is allowed to accept a fee from a patient on the practice list for the following:

☐ 196 ear piercing
☐ 197 initial treatment following a road traffic accident
☐ 198 seat belt exemption certificates
☐ 199 signing a form for the Disability Living Allowance
☐ 200 writing a letter in support of a patients housing application

Atrial fibrillation typically is a presenting feature of the following:

☐ 201 rheumatic fever
☐ 202 sarcoidosis
☐ 203 thyrotoxicosis
☐ 204 alcoholic cardiomyopathy
☐ 205 Reiter's syndrome

The following are true of normal pressure hydrocephalus:

☐ 206 cognitive impairment occurs after the onset of gait disturbance
☐ 207 a Parkinsonian gait is the typical abnormality when walking
☐ 208 urinary incontinence can be present in the absence of disturbance of gait or mental function
☐ 209 lumbar puncture is contra-indicated
☐ 210 less than 25% of patients improve after a ventricular shunt operation

Following an episode of deliberate self harm

- ☐ 211 the majority of patients will repeat one or more acts of non fatal harm within one year
- ☐ 212 provision of intensive psychiatric and social help has been shown to significantly reduce the rate of repetition
- ☐ 213 the provision of 'hotlines' (e.g. Samaritans) has significantly reduced the incidence of deliberate self harm
- ☐ 214 the majority of patients admitted to a general hospital following an episode of self harm, require transfer to a psychiatric unit
- ☐ 215 the risk of a successful suicidal attempt within the next year is approximately 10%

In polycythemia vera

- ☐ 216 splenomegaly is typical
- ☐ 217 it is associated with gout
- ☐ 218 intractable itching would cast doubt on the diagnosis
- ☐ 219 the majority eventually develop acute leukaemia
- ☐ 220 radiotherapy treatment decreases the chance of developing leukaemia

The differential diagnosis of sudden loss of vision should include the following:

- ☐ 221 migraine
- ☐ 222 central retinal vein occlusion
- ☐ 223 senile macular degeneration
- ☐ 224 optic neuritis
- ☐ 225 toxic optic neuropathy

When considering child surveillance in general practice

- ☐ 226 a child must register separately with a GP for child surveillance
- ☐ 227 child health clinics attract a health promotion clinic payment from the FHSA
- ☐ 228 child surveillance payments include an allowance for giving childhood immunisations
- ☐ 229 all GPs are eligible for inclusion in the Child Health Surveillance List
- ☐ 230 once a child is accepted onto the child surveillance list of a GP, that GP must perform all the developmental assessment

The following have been shown to be associated with an increased incidence of recurrent miscarriage:

- ☐ 231 systemic lupus erythematosus
- ☐ 232 raised levels of luteinising hormone
- ☐ 233 diabetes mellitus
- ☐ 234 thyroid disease
- ☐ 235 parental chromosomal abnormalities

Concerning acute bronchiolitis:

- ☐ 236 respiratory syncytial virus (RSV) is the most commonly isolated organism
- ☐ 237 it typically affects infants in the first year of life
- ☐ 238 it typically causes stridor
- ☐ 239 it shows a seasonal pattern
- ☐ 240 complete laryngeal obstruction is possible on examination of the throat

Following head injury there is an increased incidence of the following:

- ☐ 241 hypochondriasis
- ☐ 242 depressive illness
- ☐ 243 schizophrenia
- ☐ 244 suicide
- ☐ 245 personality disorder

When prescribing topical steroids

☐ 246 absorption is enhanced by inclusion of urea in the preparation
☐ 247 a single application to the arm of a 70 kg adult male will use approximately 4 g of preparation
☐ 248 if used continuously increase hair growth
☐ 249 ointments are indicated for most steroid responsive conditions
☐ 250 depigmentation has been shown to occur at the site of prolonged usage

Arterial leg ulceration is associated with the following:

☐ 251 pain
☐ 252 pigmentation
☐ 253 induration and oedema of the gaiter area
☐ 254 typically sited on the foot
☐ 255 punched out appearance

The following are true when considering periods:

☐ 256 the average age of onset in the UK is approximately 11 years of age
☐ 257 the average age at which patients have their last period is 50 years of age in the UK
☐ 258 the earlier periods start the later they finish
☐ 259 if the onset of periods is delayed beyond 16 years of age referral for investigation is indicated
☐ 260 estimation of LH and FSH levels is a reliable method of determining if a patient is post-menopausal

Dry eyes

☐ 261 are a cause of epiphora
☐ 262 are worse in warm weather
☐ 263 are associated with sarcoidosis
☐ 264 Sjörgren's test is diagnostic
☐ 265 are associated with entropion

The following factors would suggest a need for referring a patient with a mole to a dermatologist in order to exclude malignant change:

- ☐ 266 size less than 1 cm in diameter
- ☐ 267 an irregular outline
- ☐ 268 colour variation
- ☐ 269 erythema around the margin
- ☐ 270 scaling on the surface

Lithium carbonate

- ☐ 271 is effective in the control of schizophrenia
- ☐ 272 is available as a long acting depot preparation
- ☐ 273 is associated with increased mortality due to renal damage
- ☐ 274 is associated with abnormalities of thyroid function
- ☐ 275 is an effective agent for rapid control of symptoms

Under the access to Medical Reports Act 1988

- ☐ 276 the doctor supplying the report must receive a copy of the patient's consent
- ☐ 277 the doctor has the right to refuse to amend a report even if requested to do so by the patient
- ☐ 278 the patient has the right to view the report for up to one year after it has been sent to the insurance company or employer
- ☐ 279 the doctor can charge a fee if the patient requests a copy of the report
- ☐ 280 the doctor has the right to refuse to divulge all or part of the report to a patient

Schizoid personality disorders are associated with

- ☐ 281 being ill at ease in company
- ☐ 282 self sufficiency
- ☐ 283 obsessional behaviour
- ☐ 284 self dramatisation
- ☐ 285 lack of warmth

When considering normal distribution

☐ 286 the mean uses all information available
☐ 287 the median is easier to calculate than the mean
☐ 288 the median is not affected by extreme values
☐ 289 the mode is the value that occurs most frequently
☐ 290 variation indicates the spread of the curve

When treating undescended testes

☐ 291 no testis descends spontaneously after 1 year of age
☐ 292 all testes should be in the scrotum by 5 years of age
☐ 293 a unilateral undescended testis found after 16 years of age should be excised
☐ 294 orchidopexy has been shown to increase the chances of fertility
☐ 295 hernial sacs are present in the majority of boys at the time of orchidopexy

An elderly patient presents with symptoms of dementia, the following would suggest a depressive cause rather than Alzheimer's disease:

☐ 296 recent onset of symptoms
☐ 297 the patient continually complaining of memory loss
☐ 298 mental ability worsening in the evening
☐ 299 'don't know' as a response to many questions
☐ 300 a previous history of depressive illness

When following up patients with breast cancer

☐ 301 fixed regimes of long term follow up (5 year) by hospital have been shown to lead to a more favourable outcome
☐ 302 treatment with tamoxifen has been shown to improve prognosis in post menopausal patients
☐ 303 cancer in the opposite breast is no greater than the incidence of breast cancer for women as a whole
☐ 304 hormone manipulation has a greater response rate than chemotherapy in the management of advanced disease

A survey of adult females who have been the victims of child sexual abuse has shown that

☐ 305   the majority have some lasting psychiatric problems
☐ 306   the worst prognosis was when abuse took place repeatedly with an older man
☐ 307   they had difficulty in maintaining intimate relationships

Upon employing a new member of staff a general practitioner should be aware that they immediately have the following statutory employment rights:

☐ 308   to receive an itemized pay statement
☐ 309   to have paid time off for antenatal care
☐ 310   to be given a minimum period of notice of termination of employment
☐ 311   to receive payment for absence due to pregnancy
☐ 312   to receive a written statement of reasons for dismissal

The following are true of the use of sumatriptan in the treatment of migraine:

☐ 313   after s.c. injection of a single dose, the majority of patients will have a recurrence of headache within 48 hours
☐ 314   s.c. administration is the treatment of choice in hemiplegic migraine
☐ 315   concurrent administration with ergotamine preparations is contra-indicated
☐ 316   ventricular arrhythmias have been reported with recommended doses of the drug

When considering the organisation of care for those with gout

☐ 317   allopurinol is contra-indicated in the presence of renal calculi
☐ 318   the majority of patients with gout will have co-existing hypertension
☐ 319   lipid levels are higher in those with gout than in the general population
☐ 320   alcohol decreases the renal urate clearance
☐ 321   the majority of those with gout will have a positive family history

The following may have oral manifestations:

- ☐ 322 systemic gold therapy
- ☐ 323 bulimia
- ☐ 324 erythema multiforme
- ☐ 325 pemphigus vulgaris
- ☐ 326 lichen planus

Department of Health recommendations for influenza vaccination include adults and children in the following groups:

- ☐ 327 health care workers
- ☐ 328 patients in residential homes
- ☐ 329 patients with diabetes mellitus
- ☐ 330 patients with leukaemia
- ☐ 331 patients in heart failure

Maternity medical services

- ☐ 332 must be provided by a doctor on the obstetric list
- ☐ 333 are payable as for a full term gestation, for a live delivery occurring before 28 weeks gestation
- ☐ 334 are payable for a patient who requests and subsequently receives a therapeutic abortion from the outset of the pregnancy
- ☐ 335 the complete fee is only payable if the GP is present at the time of delivery
- ☐ 336 the fee for post natal visits is payable for visits done up to 28 days post confinement

When considering the management of upper gastrointestinal bleeding

- ☐ 337 the majority of patients will require surgery
- ☐ 338 H_2 antagonists have been shown to stop initial bleeds
- ☐ 339 the mortality rate is about 10%
- ☐ 340 gastric ulcers are more likely to bleed than duodenal ulcers
- ☐ 341 urgent endoscopic assessment at the time of hospital admission has been shown to have decreased mortality

Significant interactions have been shown to occur between the following drugs if given concurrently:

☐ 342   terfenidine and erythromycin
☐ 343   ciprofloxacin and theophyline
☐ 344   cimetidine and warfarin
☐ 345   omeprazole and alginate preparations
☐ 346   allopurinol and captopril

When considering drug abuse the following are true:

☐ 347   the majority of opiate abusers will still be addicted 7 years after starting the habit
☐ 348   methadone liquid can be injected intravenously
☐ 349   between 10-20% of opiate users will die from drug related causes
☐ 350   cocaine abuse is associated with underprivileged groups in society
☐ 351   amphetamine abuse is associated with paranoid psychosis
☐ 352   the majority of people who abuse cannabis progress to 'harder' drugs

***Candida albicans* has been implicated in the development of the following oral conditions:**

☐ 353   angular cheilitis
☐ 354   ranula
☐ 355   denture stomatitis
☐ 356   Sjörgren's syndrome

The following would suggest a diagnosis of non ulcer dyspepsia:

☐ 357   morning retching
☐ 358   night pain
☐ 359   antacid relief
☐ 360   inconsistent relationship between symptoms and food ingestion

MCQ PRACTICE PAPER 3

360 Questions : time allowed 2 hours.

An incidental finding of a raised prolactin level could be explained by

- ☐ 1 hypothyroidism
- ☐ 2 metoclopramide
- ☐ 3 pregnancy
- ☐ 4 bromocriptine
- ☐ 5 acromegaly

The following have been shown to be ototoxic:

- ☐ 6 quinine
- ☐ 7 frusemide
- ☐ 8 erythromycin
- ☐ 9 ciprofloxacin
- ☐ 10 nifedipine

A 54 year old patient presents with her periods 'restarting' after an absence of one year

- ☐ 11 an investigation is mandatory
- ☐ 12 topical oestrogens are a probable cause
- ☐ 13 cervical polyps do not cause symptoms at this age
- ☐ 14 urethral caruncles do not bleed
- ☐ 15 if accompanied by discharge this increases the likelihood of carcinoma of the cervix

Concerning coronary artery bypass grafting:

- ☐ 16 it does not improve the survival of those with persisting anginal pain at rest
- ☐ 17 operative mortality is approximately 10% in the UK
- ☐ 18 females have a higher operative risk than males
- ☐ 19 if angina is absent at one year, recurrence risk is minimal
- ☐ 20 internal mammary artery conduits produce better results than saphenous vein grafts

When diagnosing hysteria

- ☐ 21 patients have high levels of depression
- ☐ 22 amnesia occurs in the majority of people with the diagnosis
- ☐ 23 'Belle indifference' typically occurs
- ☐ 24 it characteristically occurs in later life
- ☐ 25 symptoms are associated with a psychological advantage to the patient

Mumps, measles and rubella (MMR) vaccine

- ☐ 26 more than 85% of 2 year old children have been vaccinated in the UK
- ☐ 27 the incidence of confirmed rubella in pregnancy has more than halved since introduction of the vaccine
- ☐ 28 it is contraindicated in children who are HIV positive
- ☐ 29 meningoencephalitis has been reported following exposure to the vaccine
- ☐ 30 should be used within one hour of reconstitution

Epidemiology of smoking and alcohol use in the UK

- ☐ 31 more women smoke than men
- ☐ 32 the average male smoker consumes approximately 20 cigarettes per day
- ☐ 33 cigarette smoking in children age 11-15 years of age is falling
- ☐ 34 patients with alcohol problems consult their GPs twice as often as the average patient
- ☐ 35 heavy drinkers who do not smoke have an increased incidence of cancers

When considering post viral fatigue syndrome

- ☐ 36 fatigue is the second most common reason to consult the doctor by the general population
- ☐ 37 delayed fatigue developing after exertion would suggest a different diagnosis
- ☐ 38 the majority of patients have no psychopathology
- ☐ 39 depression is the most common psychiatric disorder
- ☐ 40 prolonged rest is the treatment of choice

A patient presents with acute onset of a painful, photophobic red eye with impairment of vision. The following are possible diagnoses:

☐ 41 episcleritis
☐ 42 iritis
☐ 43 keratitis
☐ 44 sub-conjunctival haemorrhage
☐ 45 glaucoma

The differential diagnosis of a pustular rash occurring on the palms of the hands should include

☐ 46 infected eczema
☐ 47 scabies
☐ 48 pustular psoriasis
☐ 49 ichthyosis
☐ 50 erythema multiforme

A one year old child without diarrhoea attends the surgery, the following would suggest significant dehydration:

☐ 51 crying with tears
☐ 52 visible weight loss
☐ 53 bradycardia
☐ 54 dry mouth
☐ 55 irritability

A 20 year old patient with asthma rapidly becomes more dyspnoeic

☐ 56 the extent of rhonchi predicts the severity of the attack
☐ 57 pneumothorax typically occurs in this age group
☐ 58 tachycardia is a reliable predictor of severity
☐ 59 peak flow levels are unreliable in judging severe disease
☐ 60 the majority of acute attacks develop within 24 hours of the first symptom

Obesity is associated with the following conditions:

☐ 61 hiatus hernia
☐ 62 endometrial carcinoma
☐ 63 hyperlipidaemia
☐ 64 infertility
☐ 65 hypertension

The following additional factors would indicate significant pathology with the presentation of headaches around the eye:

☐ 66 haloes around lights
☐ 67 sleep disturbances due to the headache
☐ 68 a red eye
☐ 69 amblyopia
☐ 70 a pale optic disc

In alcohol withdrawal syndrome

☐ 71 the risk of developing symptoms is related to the amount of intake
☐ 72 seizures typically occur within the first 12 hours after stopping drinking
☐ 73 delirium tremens has a mortality in excess of 20%
☐ 74 auditory hallucinations occurring after 72 hours of the last alcohol intake would signify that there was some other pathology
☐ 75 withdrawal symptoms typically commence within 3-6 hours of the last drink

Sudden infant death syndrome is associated with the following:

☐ 76 a difficult delivery in labour
☐ 77 a mother addicted to narcotic agents
☐ 78 a decreasing risk with greater parity
☐ 79 sleeping in a prone position
☐ 80 being a twin

When treating scabies with gamma benzene hexachloride (Quellada)

☐ 81 the application should be preceded by a hot bath
☐ 82 it is contra-indicated in pregnant women
☐ 83 itching that fails to resolve two weeks after treatment is an indication for a further application
☐ 84 a single application left in contact with the skin has been shown to be adequate treatment
☐ 85 treatment of the face is essential if all the mites are to be eradicated

Concerning Hodgkin's disease:

☐ 86 it most commonly presents with a fever
☐ 87 cervical lymph nodes are most commonly involved
☐ 88 hepatomegaly is a typical finding at presentation
☐ 89 chemotherapy is the most appropriate treatment for localised disease
☐ 90 the majority of patients can be cured

Agoraphobic patients

☐ 91 are typically female
☐ 92 have a higher incidence of marital problems than the general population
☐ 93 typically have a fear of fainting
☐ 94 if they report depersonalisation this would indicate other pathology
☐ 95 show a good response to aversion therapy

Fixed drug eruptions

☐ 96 always occur at the same site with a specific drug
☐ 97 appear within 5-10 minutes of administration
☐ 98 discolouration of the skin remains for several months
☐ 99 blistering in the lesions makes the diagnosis unlikely
☐ 100 have well defined borders

You decide that your present premises are inadequate and wish to move to a new property

☐ 101 improvement grants can be used to help towards the construction of new premises
☐ 102 if you are a training practice a separate room must be provided for the trainee
☐ 103 the cost rent scheme limits the size of the consultation rooms
☐ 104 notional rent is paid by the FHSA to reimburse existing GPs for capital tied up in their own surgery
☐ 105 once a practice undertakes a cost rent scheme it is unable to change back to notional rent reimbursement

Concerning paracetamol overdosage:

☐ 106 ingestion of 10 g is associated with the development of liver damage
☐ 107 chronic alcohol ingestion protects against liver damage
☐ 108 antidote therapy is ineffective if given more than 15 hours after the overdose
☐ 109 patients on carbamazepine are at greater risk of toxic effects
☐ 110 mortality has significantly decreased in the last 10 years

The Access to Health Records Act 1990

☐ 111 provides rights of access to computer held records only
☐ 112 health visitor records are exempt
☐ 113 there is no right of access to notes made before November 1991
☐ 114 a doctor has 21 days to respond to a request for access
☐ 115 a fee may be charged for allowing a patient access

The following statements are true of cardiac valve disease in the elderly:

☐ 116 aortic stenosis is the commonest valve lesion
☐ 117 a soft murmur excludes aortic stenosis
☐ 118 rheumatic heart disease is the cause of the majority of cases of mitral stenosis
☐ 119 prolapsed mitral valve is the main cause of mitral regurgitation
☐ 120 the majority of patients over 70 years of age have a murmur

The following are high risk factors for osteoporosis:

- ☐ 121 late menarche
- ☐ 122 early menopause
- ☐ 123 nulliparity
- ☐ 124 alcoholism
- ☐ 125 high salt consumption

In mental retardation due to fragile X syndrome

- ☐ 126 the majority of mothers are mildly mentally handicapped
- ☐ 127 bat ears are associated
- ☐ 128 it can be detected antenatally
- ☐ 129 infantile autism is associated
- ☐ 130 there is a male predominance

The regulations governing the availability of general practitioners under the terms of service, include the following:

- ☐ 131 full time unrestricted GPs must be available to patients for a minimum of 26 hours per week
- ☐ 132 GPs must be available for 45 weeks per year
- ☐ 133 the times of availability must be approved by the FHSA
- ☐ 134 job sharing GPs must still be available for 5 days per week
- ☐ 135 the hours of availability to patients includes travelling time

The following drugs undergo significant first pass metabolism:

- ☐ 136 salbutamol
- ☐ 137 paracetamol
- ☐ 138 codeine
- ☐ 139 metoclopramide
- ☐ 140 acyclovir

During the normal ovulatory cycle

☐ 141 after ovulation, cervical mucus is a watery, stretchy, transparent secretion
☐ 142 during ovulation the os will admit the tip of a finger
☐ 143 basal body temperature is higher in the luteal phase
☐ 144 after ovulation the cervix remains soft to the touch
☐ 145 ovulation predictor tests measure oestrogenic surge

Concerning Parkinson's disease:

☐ 146 tremor is the most prominent feature of Parkinsonism in the elderly
☐ 147 it has a prevalence of approximately 1 in 1000 in the elderly
☐ 148 prolonged use of levodopa is associated with 'freezing' episodes
☐ 149 selegiline is only suitable for patients who no longer respond to levodopa
☐ 150 it does not cause cognitive impairment

When considering fibroids

☐ 151 spontaneous shrinkage takes place at the menopause
☐ 152 hormone replacement therapy has been shown to stimulate growth of fibroids
☐ 153 gonadotrophin releasing hormone analogues cause significant decrease in the size of fibroids
☐ 154 gonadotrophin releasing hormone analogues cause increased bone loss
☐ 155 surgery is indicated for fibroids which have a size over that of a 14-16 week gestation

The following have been shown to trigger anxiety states:

☐ 156 monoamine oxidase inhibitors
☐ 157 hypoglycaemia
☐ 158 severe angina
☐ 159 caffeine
☐ 160 paroxysmal atrial tachycardia

Teratogenicity has been shown to occur as follows with the drugs listed:

☐ 161 sodium valproate has been shown to be associated with an increased risk of spina bifida
☐ 162 phenytoin is associated with congenital heart disease
☐ 163 carbamazepine is associated with bone marrow depression
☐ 164 lithium carbonate is associated with congenital heart disease
☐ 165 heparin is associated with central nervous system defects

Acute suppurative otitis media

☐ 166 has a peak incidence at 2-3 years of age
☐ 167 is commoner in smoking households
☐ 168 is commoner in atopic individuals
☐ 169 the majority are bacterial in origin
☐ 170 approximately 5% will develop mastoiditis

Concerning pulmonary embolism in pregnancy:

☐ 171 the majority of cases occur antenatally
☐ 172 primigravidae are more at risk than belle multigravidae
☐ 173 patients with a previous history of thromboembolism should have prophylactic treatment throughout the pregnancy
☐ 174 it is the commonest cause of maternal death in the UK
☐ 175 those who have an instrumental delivery are at greater risk of a postnatal embolism than those who deliver normally

In acute appendicitis

☐ 176 increasing dietary fibre has been shown to decrease the incidence of the condition
☐ 177 it occurs in more than 10% of the population
☐ 178 the majority of elderly patients have perforated by the time they reach surgery
☐ 179 the majority of children have perforated by the time they reach surgery
☐ 180 retrocaecal appendices are associated with classic symptoms

Concerning consent in the United Kingdom:

☐ 181 all material risks to a patient must be given
☐ 182 information about a risk can only be withheld if it would pose a serious threat of psychological detriment to the patient
☐ 183 consent must be given in writing
☐ 184 patients under 16 years of age are able to give consent
☐ 185 for taking intimate samples under the Police and Criminal Evidence Act, parental consent is needed for those under 17 years of age

Under the terms of the 1990 contract a general practitioner will be reimbursed for the following minor surgical procedures:

☐ 186 insertion of a hormonal implant
☐ 187 colposcopy
☐ 188 injection of a frozen shoulder with depot steroids
☐ 189 removal of a nasal foreign body
☐ 190 liquid nitrogen applied to a verruca

Concerning leukaemia in childhood:

☐ 191 the peak incidence is between 7-12 years of age
☐ 192 the majority are acute myeloblastic leukaemia
☐ 193 the majority of patients with acute lymphoblastic leukaemia will survive 5 years after cessation of therapy
☐ 194 maintenance cytotoxics are usually needed for about 3 years
☐ 195 the average GP will see one new case every 200 years

When prescribing hormone replacement therapy the following are true:

☐ 196 diabetes is an absolute contraindication to treatment
☐ 197 oestradiol implants have been shown not to improve atrophic vaginitis
☐ 198 breakthrough bleeding whilst on treatment can be safely ignored
☐ 199 unopposed oestrogen therapy has an adverse effect on lipid levels
☐ 200 to be effective in the treatment of osteoporosis, it should be given for approximately 10 years

Concerning impotence in men:

- ☐ 201 if of sudden onset is more likely to be organic
- ☐ 202 is commoner in those with peripheral arterial disease
- ☐ 203 when treated with papaverine, it is given into the dorsal vein of the penis
- ☐ 204 an erection produced by papaverine typically lasts 12 hours
- ☐ 205 vacuum condoms are available on NHS prescription

The senile squalor syndrome (Diogenes syndrome)

- ☐ 206 typically affects married couples
- ☐ 207 the majority have significant psychiatric illness
- ☐ 208 is significantly associated with heavy alcohol intake
- ☐ 209 rapidly improves on admission to hospital
- ☐ 210 patients are of above average intelligence

Pulled elbow

- ☐ 211 affects children of pre-school age
- ☐ 212 is caused by a fall on the outstretched hand
- ☐ 213 requires operative reduction
- ☐ 214 X-rays show a characteristic appearance
- ☐ 215 is commoner on the left than the right

When differentiating between ulcerative colitis and Crohn's disease, the following are true:

- ☐ 216 rectal bleeding is commoner in Crohn's disease
- ☐ 217 rectal involvement is present in the majority of patients with ulcerative colitis
- ☐ 218 strictures are a frequent occurrence in ulcerative colitis
- ☐ 219 abdominal pain is typical of Crohn's disease
- ☐ 220 the majority of patients with Crohn's disease present with diarrhoea

Over 75 health checks

☐ 221   receive an item of service payment from the FHSA
☐ 222   have to be performed every three years
☐ 223   the majority of over 75 year olds would not otherwise see their GP on a regular basis
☐ 224   the cost benefit of screening is now well established
☐ 225   approximately half the screened population will have undiscovered illness or undiscovered social deprivation

Concerning squint:

☐ 226   it is a typical presentation of retinoblastoma
☐ 227   paralytic squints are commoner in children than adults
☐ 228   operative treatment will correct amblyopia at the age of 8 years
☐ 229   patching can lead to amblyopia in the 'good' eye
☐ 230   cooperation of the child is necessary before considering referral

Oral contraceptives confer the following gynaecological benefits:

☐ 231   decreased incidence of cervical erosion
☐ 232   suppression of benign breast disease
☐ 233   decrease in ovarian cancer
☐ 234   decrease in endometrial cancer
☐ 235   decreased risk of carcinoma in situ of the cervix

A 30 year old female patient presents with episodes of vomiting, the following would suggest a diagnosis of Addison's disease:

☐ 236   abdominal pain
☐ 237   weight loss
☐ 238   hypokalaemia
☐ 239   very low blood urea
☐ 240   hypertension

The incidence of dementia has been shown to be reduced by

- ☐ 241 social support of the bereaved
- ☐ 242 a well balanced diet
- ☐ 243 avoidance of beef
- ☐ 244 treatment of hypertension
- ☐ 245 over 75 screening by general practitioners

Restless legs

- ☐ 246 are a familial complaint
- ☐ 247 show a tendency to worsen in the evening
- ☐ 248 are worsened by benzodiazepine hypnotics
- ☐ 249 an association with systemic disease has not been shown
- ☐ 250 is associated with excessive coffee ingestion

Audit

- ☐ 251 is prescriptive
- ☐ 252 is a passive process
- ☐ 253 is looking for mistakes
- ☐ 254 is solely concerned with problem solving
- ☐ 255 the boundaries between audit and research are clear cut

The following drugs are available without a doctor's prescription:

- ☐ 256 terfenadine tablets
- ☐ 257 glyceryl trinitrate tablets
- ☐ 258 chloroquine tablets
- ☐ 259 miconazole cream
- ☐ 260 pyridoxine 50 mg tablets

Acute pyelonephritis in pregnancy

- ☐ 261 typically presents in the first trimester
- ☐ 262 reoccurs in approximately one quarter of cases
- ☐ 263 is associated with an increased chance of pre-term labour
- ☐ 264 is associated with fetal growth retardation
- ☐ 265 ciprofloxin is indicated for treatment

A 23 year old male presents with low back pain, the following would support a diagnosis of ankylosing spondylitis:

- ☐ 266 early morning stiffness in the back
- ☐ 267 raised ESR
- ☐ 268 an associated peripheral arthritis
- ☐ 269 a recent history of painful red eye
- ☐ 270 a positive family history

The following conditions cause skin rashes that are intensely itchy:

- ☐ 271 dermatitis artefacta
- ☐ 272 polymorphic eruption of pregnancy
- ☐ 273 nodular prurigo
- ☐ 274 dermatitis herpetiformis
- ☐ 275 lichen simplex

Puerperal psychosis

- ☐ 276 typically presents by the 10th day following delivery
- ☐ 277 typically, it presents with mania, eventually becoming depressive
- ☐ 278 is associated with an increased risk of infanticide
- ☐ 279 ECT has been shown to be of no value in treatment
- ☐ 280 typically remits within 2-3 months

Adult gastrointestinal infections have been shown to have the following characteristics:

- [ ] 281 campylobacter typically produces a febrile illness
- [ ] 282 shigella is associated with blood in the stools
- [ ] 283 giardia produces severe colicky pain
- [ ] 284 salmonella without blood stream invasion lasts 3-4 days
- [ ] 285 salmonella with blood stream invasion typically lasts 7-10 days

When considering fibrinolytic drugs in myocardial infarction

- [ ] 286 streptokinase is given by IV bolus injection
- [ ] 287 the use of aspirin is contraindicated for 12 months after use of streptokinase
- [ ] 288 fibrinolytic drugs are contraindicated in patients over 80 years of age
- [ ] 289 streptokinase can be repeated 3 months after initial use if a second infarct develops at that time
- [ ] 290 a recently diagnosed duodenal ulcer is a contraindication to the use of a fibrinolytic

The following are true of developmental milestones in a normal child:

- [ ] 291 at 6 weeks the Moro reflex is still retained
- [ ] 292 at 7 months the majority can stand without support
- [ ] 293 at 12 months they can say 3 words with meaning
- [ ] 294 at 30 months the majority will be dry at night
- [ ] 295 at 54 months the majority can dress themselves

Hypertrophic cardiomyopathy

- [ ] 296 is an inherited disorder
- [ ] 297 is typically a disease of old age
- [ ] 298 characteristically presents with shortness of breath
- [ ] 299 is the commonest cause of sudden death in athletes
- [ ] 300 electrocardiographic changes are typical

A 32 year old female patient presents with acute onset of neck pains of musculo-skeletal origin. It has been shown that at this age

☐ 301 the majority of patients are pain free after one month
☐ 302 the majority of patients will have recurrence of pain within 2 years
☐ 303 soft cervical collars are of proven benefit in reducing the duration of symptoms
☐ 304 non steroidal anti inflammatory drugs have been shown to be of benefit in reducing the duration of symptoms
☐ 305 manipulative techniques (e.g. Cyriax) have been shown to be of no additional benefit

Corneal ulcers due to herpes simplex infection

☐ 306 recur in the majority of cases
☐ 307 if associated with anterior uveitis may lead to secondary glaucoma
☐ 308 typically need treatment with acyclovir for more than 2 weeks
☐ 309 visual acuity is decreased in the majority of patients
☐ 310 have a characteristic appearance on staining the cornea with fluorescein
☐ 311 are typically painless

Chlamydial infection

☐ 312 typically causes a vaginitis
☐ 313 is asymptomatic in the majority of women
☐ 314 is the commonest cause of chronic prostatitis
☐ 315 if discovered in pregnancy is best left untreated until after delivery
☐ 316 associated urethritis is typically associated with a dysuria and a negative midstream urine culture

Epidemiology of backache in the United Kingdom

☐ 317 more than 10 million working days are lost per year
☐ 318 the average general practitioner sees less than 30 acute backs per year
☐ 319 the majority recover within one month without treatment
☐ 320 less than 1 in 200 undergo surgery
☐ 321 rest in the initial stages of treatment has been shown to reduce the overall time away from work

The following have been shown to trigger attacks of irritable bowel syndrome:

- ☐ 322 metronidazole
- ☐ 323 wheat bran
- ☐ 324 milk
- ☐ 325 nystatin
- ☐ 326 stress

Nocturnal cramps have been shown to be caused by

- ☐ 327 cirrhosis of the liver
- ☐ 328 venous obstruction
- ☐ 329 peripheral arterial disease
- ☐ 330 L5/S1 disc compression
- ☐ 331 salbutamol administration

Concerning breast feeding:

- ☐ 332 UK government health targets for the year 2000 include one that 75% of babies are to be breast fed
- ☐ 333 mastitis is typically caused by streptococcus
- ☐ 334 typically takes longer than bottle feeding
- ☐ 335 causes babies to be obese with the same frequency as bottle feeding
- ☐ 336 weaning onto cows milk should take place at 6 months of age

When considering the drug treatment of asthma with inhaler devices

- ☐ 337 the incidence of oral candidiasis is increased by the use of spacer devices
- ☐ 338 salmeterol is indicated for p.r.n. usage
- ☐ 339 intermittent terbutaline has been shown to lead to long term worsening of asthma
- ☐ 340 steroid dosage of 600 mg daily has been shown to be associated with adrenal suppression in adults
- ☐ 341 sodium cromoglycate is of no proven value in treating acute asthmatic attacks

Basic practice allowance

☐ 342   is not paid to partners who work less than full time
☐ 343   must be claimed annually
☐ 344   is paid in full to a singlehanded GP with a list of 1000 patients
☐ 345   in a group practice the total list size is used to calculate the eligibility
for the allowance

Active management of the third stage of labour by use of controlled cord traction and oxytocic drugs has been shown to be associated with

☐ 346   a shorter third stage of labour
☐ 347   a decreased incidence of post partum haemorrhage
☐ 348   an increased incidence of retained placenta
☐ 349   an increased incidence of post partum hypertension
☐ 350   an increased incidence of post partum vomiting

Amitriptyline has been shown to be of benefit in the treatment of

☐ 351   post viral fatigue syndrome
☐ 352   Bell's palsy
☐ 353   post herpetic neuralgia
☐ 354   irritable bowel syndrome
☐ 355   migraine

A baby is diagnosed as having a patent ductus arteriosus at 7 days of age. The following are true:

☐ 356   closure typically takes place within 48 hours of birth
☐ 357   prematurity is associated with delay in closure
☐ 358   indomethacin has been shown to promote closure
☐ 359   without treatment the majority of patients will die before 30 years
of age
☐ 360   infective endocarditis rarely complicates the condition

360 Questions : time allowed 2 hours.

The following factors have been shown to have adverse prognostic significance in the acute stage of stroke:

- ☐ 1 pre-existing treated hypertension
- ☐ 2 bilateral extensor plantar responses
- ☐ 3 impaired level of consciousness
- ☐ 4 previous myocardial infarction
- ☐ 5 inability to walk

Polycystic ovary syndrome

- ☐ 6 is detectable by ultrasound
- ☐ 7 is associated with oligomenorrhea
- ☐ 8 has an increased risk of early miscarriage
- ☐ 9 has a raised LH/FSH ratio
- ☐ 10 associated hirsutism responds to cyproterone acetate

Concerning head lice:

- ☐ 11 the overall incidence is declining in the UK
- ☐ 12 resistance to standard preparations has not emerged
- ☐ 13 shampoos are more effective than lotions
- ☐ 14 treatment with carbaryl confers a residual protective effect
- ☐ 15 malathion is inactivated by swimming in chlorinated water
- ☐ 16 nit combing is essential if the disease is to be eradicated

Recent weight loss of over 5% in a patient over 65 has been shown to be associated with

- ☐ 17 physical illness in the majority of cases
- ☐ 18 malignancy in approximately 20%
- ☐ 19 the reason for the weight loss being usually apparent at the initial examination
- ☐ 20 follow up being indicated in those with no apparent pathology
- ☐ 21 the majority of those without obvious pathology increasing their weight within one year

You have a 68 year old woman in the practice with a diagnosis of 'pernicious anaemia'. She is maintained on monthly injections of hydroxocobalamin. On reviewing her case the following are true:

☐ 22 a Schilling test cannot be performed now that B12 stores are replete
☐ 23 dietary deficiency is more common than autoimmune gastric atrophy
☐ 24 dependency upon B12 is unknown
☐ 25 hydroxocobalamin is usually given every 3 months
☐ 26 excessive administration of B12 causes harmful side effects

Wood's light

☐ 27 is a source of infrared light
☐ 28 causes eczematous skin to fluoresce pink
☐ 29 causes scalp ringworm to fluoresce green
☐ 30 will detect complete loss of pigment in vitiligo
☐ 31 will help differentiate common warts from seborrhoeic warts

Depression in the elderly has been shown to be associated with

☐ 32 delusions of poverty
☐ 33 pseudodementia
☐ 34 a closer association with bereavement than in younger patients
☐ 35 agitation
☐ 36 retardation

Concerning cryotherapy:

☐ 37 the majority of children of 5 years of age can tolerate cryotherapy
☐ 38 basal cell carcinomas are unsuitable for treatment
☐ 39 if a 'triple response' occurs the treatment should not be used again
☐ 40 local swelling means the length of application was excessive
☐ 41 liquid nitrogen destroys viruses

Prescriptions are issued free to patients with the following conditions:

- ☐ 42 rheumatoid arthritis
- ☐ 43 chronic glaucoma
- ☐ 44 asthma
- ☐ 45 myxoedema
- ☐ 46 hyperthyroidism

Concerning accidents in children:

- ☐ 47 they are the commonest cause of death in the 1-15 age group
- ☐ 48 the majority of accidental deaths occur in the home
- ☐ 49 every year 1:10 children will attend the doctor with an accidental injury
- ☐ 50 preventative education has been shown to save lives
- ☐ 51 5% of accidental poisonings are fatal

Hypertensive retinopathy has the following features:

- ☐ 52 cotton wool spots are a feature of grade III retinopathy
- ☐ 53 the changes associated with grade II retinopathy are reversible with good hypertensive control
- ☐ 54 retinal haemorrhages associated with retinopathy typically interfere with vision
- ☐ 55 papilloedema due to hypertension is indistinguishable from that due to raised intracranial pressure
- ☐ 56 arterio-venous crossing changes indicate arteriosclerosis

Pacemakers are associated with

- ☐ 57 a restriction in activity
- ☐ 58 the majority are implanted for the treatment of complete heart block
- ☐ 59 unreliable ECG appearances in the event of a myocardial infarction
- ☐ 60 post implant the commonest cause of death is primary pacemaker failure
- ☐ 61 a lifespan of the pacemaker of at least 5 years

The following would suggest an atypical grief reaction:

- ☐ 62 onset of distress delayed until 4 weeks after the death
- ☐ 63 open hostility to relatives
- ☐ 64 extreme social isolation
- ☐ 65 absence from work for 6 weeks
- ☐ 66 non-specific suicidal ideas

You are consulted by the parents of a 5 year old boy recently diagnosed as having cystic fibrosis

- ☐ 67 late diagnosis implies medical neglect
- ☐ 68 there is a 1:2 chance of subsequent children being affected
- ☐ 69 the majority of patients with this condition will die by late teenage
- ☐ 70 affected boys are usually azoospermic
- ☐ 71 affected adolescents have an increased incidence of glucose intolerance

In carpal tunnel syndrome

- ☐ 72 pain radiating to the shoulder excludes the diagnosis
- ☐ 73 it typically affects the dominant hand
- ☐ 74 local steroid injections typically worsen the pain
- ☐ 75 it is associated with hypothyroidism
- ☐ 76 thenar wasting is a characteristic feature

A 63 year old man has a high ESR, the following would support a diagnosis of myeloma:

- ☐ 77 hypercalcaemia
- ☐ 78 osteosclerotic lesions on X-ray
- ☐ 79 rouleaux on a peripheral blood film
- ☐ 80 peripheral neuropathy
- ☐ 81 unexplained bruising

Concerning endometriosis:

☐ 82 ectopic endometrium is found in the majority of patients who have a laparoscopy for infertility

☐ 83 medical treatment of endometriosis has been shown to improve future fertility

☐ 84 pain is proportional to the extent of the disease

☐ 85 cyclical pain casts doubt on the diagnosis

☐ 86 medical treatment rarely causes an improvement within 6 months

When considering multiple sclerosis

☐ 87 the peak age of onset is about 30 years of age

☐ 88 there is no hereditary disposition

☐ 89 the majority of patients have full remission after the first attack

☐ 90 specific diagnostic tests are now available

☐ 91 the mean life expectancy is over 30 years after the presenting complaint

The Childrens Act 1989 states that

☐ 92 Emergency Protection orders have a maximum duration of 8 days

☐ 93 only social workers can apply for an Emergency Protection order on a child

☐ 94 parental access is precluded during an Emergency Protection order

☐ 95 care orders and supervision orders are mutually exclusive

☐ 96 police protection provisions allow parental responsibility to be transferred to the police

In acute torticollis

☐ 97 it typically occurs in the over 40 year age group

☐ 98 it indicates underlying cervical arthritic changes

☐ 99 only active movements are limited

☐ 100 pain typically increases in intensity throughout the day

☐ 101 the neck is typically flexed towards the painful side

When considering inhaled corticosteroids

☐ 102 nebulised steroids are more efficient than metered dose inhalers
☐ 103 adrenal suppression in adults has been shown to occur with a total daily dose of 1000 micrograms
☐ 104 larger volume spacer devices increase oropharyngeal deposition
☐ 105 inhibition of growth in children using 800 micrograms daily has been reported

Concerning urinary tract infections in children:

☐ 106 the majority have no structural abnormality
☐ 107 10% of children will have had an infection by the time they are 10 years of age
☐ 108 the commonest abnormal finding is vesico-ureteric reflux
☐ 109 approximately half will present with non specific symptoms under the age of 2 years
☐ 110 may present as a diarrhoeal illness

The following are true of infective endocarditis:

☐ 111 mitral valve prolapse is a risk factor
☐ 112 the route of the infecting organism is obvious in the majority of cases
☐ 113 the mortality is minimal once treatment commences
☐ 114 anaemia is a typical finding
☐ 115 the plasma viscosity is typically elevated

When looking at nails which are discoloured the following are true:

☐ 116 penicillamine stains nails yellow
☐ 117 an irregular yellow area associated with a thickened nail plate is typically due to tinea infection
☐ 118 familial leuconychia causes small white streaks on the nails
☐ 119 yellow nail syndrome is associated with lymphoedema elsewhere in the body
☐ 120 chloroquine stains nails green

Concerning research in general practice:

☐ 121 research protocols typically contain the curriculum vitae of the researcher

☐ 122 ethical committees have no interest in the source of finance for a research project

☐ 123 all risks must be made known to the participating patients

☐ 124 retrospective studies from patients records require consent from the patient concerned

☐ 125 structured interviews have been shown to need specialist interviewers to obtain accurate results

When considering meningococcal meningitis

☐ 126 vaccine is effective against all strains

☐ 127 prevalence is decreasing

☐ 128 resistance of strains to penicillin has emerged

☐ 129 chloramphenicol is the chemoprophylactic agent of choice

☐ 130 immediate family members have a minimally increased risk of contracting the disease from an infected house member

In bulimia nervosa

☐ 131 the majority of patients with this condition are underweight

☐ 132 drug treatment has been shown to be less effective than intensive psychological treatments

☐ 133 fetal abnormalities have been shown to be more common in those patients who have bulimia

☐ 134 if associated with anorexia it carries a worse prognosis

☐ 135 it is associated with diuretic abuse

Your practice is unsure whether to give iron supplements routinely in pregnancy. In discussing the matter the following are true:

T 136 plasma ferritin levels accurately reflect maternal iron stores
T 137 neonatal iron stores are acquired in the last trimester
T 138 iron supplementation has been shown to reduce iron depletion
F 139 iron requirements are greatest in the first trimester
F 140 ferrous salts have a higher incidence of side effects than the other iron salts

Opiate analgesics have been shown to interact with the following:

T 141 paracetamol
T 142 chlorpromazine
T 143 phenytoin
T 144 cimetidine
T 145 lactulose

Contraceptive fees are payable

T 146 if a practice nurse fits a diaphragm
F 147 if a temporary resident requesting emergency contraception signs an Immediate and Necessary treatment form
T 148 if the doctor gives the patient advice only
F 149 if a female patient seeks advice about her partner having a vasectomy
F 150 if a GP performs a vasectomy

The following are true of general practice in the United Kingdom:

T 151 the average list size of a GP is less than 2000 patients
T 152 the majority of GPs practice in partnerships of four or more doctors
T 153 approximately 25% of UK practices are recognised for vocational training
F 154 the majority of GPs practice from Health Centres
F 155 the average GP sees more than 150 patients per week in the surgery

In Gilbert's syndrome

T □ 156 it occurs in more than 2% of the population
F □ 157 a liver biopsy shows abnormal histology
F □ 158 jaundice is worsened after a large meal
F □ 159 it is associated with development of gall stones
F □ 160 it is associated with a decreased life expectancy

Depressive disorders are typically associated with

F □ 161 feeling worse in the evening
T □ 162 an abnormal dexamethasone suppression test
T □ 163 delusions of poverty
T □ 164 amenorrhoea
F □ 165 difficulty in falling asleep

Normal adolescence is characterised by the following:

T □ 166 the first sign of puberty in boys is testicular growth
F □ 167 the first sign of puberty in girls is the appearance of pubic hair
F □ 168 the major part of weight gain is due to deposition of fat
T □ 169 girls are ahead of boys in all aspects of pubertal development
T □ 170 full stature is achieved approximately 4 years after the peak growth spurt

A 30 year old female patient presents with a febrile illness and tender red nodular lesions on the lower legs. The following are probable diagnoses:

F □ 171 Lyme disease
F □ 172 erysipelas
T □ 173 erythema nodosum
F □ 174 acantosis nigricans
F □ 175 Kaposi's sarcoma

In hypothermia

☐ 176 immersion in water as a cause of hypothermia increases the probability of death

☐ 177 cardiac arrhythmias do not occur until the body temperature of 33 centigrade

☐ 178 unconsciousness typically occurs below a temperature of 33 centigrade

☐ 179 confusion is feature of a core temperature of 34 centigrade

☐ 180 rewarming should occur at the same rate at which a patient becomes cold

When considering cataract surgery

☐ 181 it is more successful if performed at a later stage

☐ 182 it increases the risk of retinal detachment

☐ 183 thickening of the posterior capsule is a complication of intracapsular extraction

☐ 184 bed rest is required for 24 hours post operatively

☐ 185 intra-ocular implants are only suitable for myopic patients

The following are true of angiotensin converting enzyme inhibitors:

☐ 186 drug induced cough typically resolves if treatment is continued

☐ 187 they are associated with intra-uterine death

☐ 188 lithium carbonate toxicity is potentiated

☐ 189 hyponatraemia only occurs if they are given concurrently with diuretics

☐ 190 skin rashes occur in less than 1% of patients

A 15 year old girl presents with anterior knee pain, a diagnosis of chondromalacia patella would be supported by

☐ 191 pain on pressing the patella

☐ 192 pain worse on ascending stairs rather than on descending

☐ 193 palpable crepitus on passive movements

☐ 194 a normal 'skyline' knee X-ray

☐ 195 hyperextension of the knee joint by 10 degrees or more

The practice annual report must contain the following information before submission to the FHSA:

- ☐ 196 the numbers of patients who self referred themselves to the local casualty department
- ☐ 197 a list of courses attended by the GPs
- ☐ 198 the names of all staff employed
- ☐ 199 the changes planned during the next year
- ☐ 200 the number of referrals made to the genito-urinary clinic
- ☐ 201 the arrangements by which patients may comment on the service available

Delusions

- ☐ 202 are diagnostic of schizophrenia
- ☐ 203 can be modified by contrary experience
- ☐ 204 are obsessions
- ☐ 205 are false ideas
- ☐ 206 can be secondary to hallucinations

Hypothyroidism is associated with

- ☐ 207 a gruff voice
- ☐ 208 pretibial myxoedema
- ☐ 209 anaemia
- ☐ 210 muscle cramps
- ☐ 211 a malar flush

Concerning opiate addiction

- ☐ 212 doctors not licensed may prescribe methadone to a drug addict
- ☐ 213 a central register of opiate addicts is maintained
- ☐ 214 withdrawal symptoms commence 12 hours after the last dose of methadone
- ☐ 215 convulsions are associated with rapid withdrawal

A patient requests a home confinement. In responding to her the following are true:

- ☐ 216 fetal monitoring of low risk cases decreases morbidity in the baby
- ☐ 217 a doctor must be present at a home confinement
- ☐ 218 an abnormal delivery is commoner in lower social classes
- ☐ 219 the majority of babies require some form of specialised assistance at or shortly after birth
- ☐ 220 a general practitioner is under a contractual obligation to provide home care if the patient insists on a domiciliary confinement

Snoring has been shown to be associated with

- ☐ 221 enlarged tonsils
- ☐ 222 hypothyroidism
- ☐ 223 excessive daytime sleepiness
- ☐ 224 morning headaches
- ☐ 225 systemic hypertension

A patient of another practice in your town decides to register with you

- ☐ 226 responsibility for this patient does not commence until the 10th day after signing the initial registration form
- ☐ 227 the patient must be offered a health check in writing
- ☐ 228 new patient health checks attract an item of service payment
- ☐ 229 you must complete the health check at the time of registration
- ☐ 230 a separate fee is claimable for immunisations given at the time of registration

Concerning ciprofloxacin:

- ☐ 231 aluminium-containing antacids interfere with absorption
- ☐ 232 theophylline levels are elevated if the two drugs are given concurrently
- ☐ 233 it is ineffective against *Pseudomonas aeroginosa*
- ☐ 234 it has been shown to be less active in acid urine
- ☐ 235 it has been shown to be more effective than doxycycline in the treatment of chlamydia

In laparoscopic cholecystectomy

- ☐ 236 it is only suitable for a minority of patients with gall stones
- ☐ 237 the operative time is longer
- ☐ 238 return to work is earlier
- ☐ 239 post-operative complications are more frequent
- ☐ 240 a nasogastric tube needs to be passed pre operatively

The following are true of pre-eclampsia:

- ☐ 241 proteinuria is an early feature
- ☐ 242 circadian rhythm of blood pressure is reversed
- ☐ 243 90% of normal pregnant women have oedema at term
- ☐ 244 early control of blood pressure has been shown to retard its progression
- ☐ 245 is associated with placental abruption

Seborrhoeic eczema in infancy

- ☐ 246 has a peak age of onset under 3 months of age
- ☐ 247 is typically itchy
- ☐ 248 resolves spontaneously in the majority of children
- ☐ 249 typically fails to respond to emollients
- ☐ 250 characteristically involves the flexures

The following would support a diagnosis of maxillary sinusitis:

- ☐ 251 swelling of the cheek
- ☐ 252 pain in the teeth
- ☐ 253 pain worse on bending
- ☐ 254 clear nasal discharge
- ☐ 255 tenderness over the maxillary antrum

Health visitors

- [ ] 256 must have a post basic training in paediatric nursing
- [ ] 257 must have a post basic training in obstetrics
- [ ] 258 the majority conduct over 75 screening on behalf of general practitioners
- [ ] 259 have a statutory obligation to visit post natally on the 1st day after discharge from hospital
- [ ] 260 have self employed status

The following statements are true of eye disease:

- [ ] 261 recurrent chalazia are associated with acne rosacea
- [ ] 262 blepharitis is common in patients with psoriasis
- [ ] 263 correction of entropion requires an operation under general anaesthetic
- [ ] 264 alkalis are less damaging than acids if accidentally splashed into the eye
- [ ] 265 Kaposi's sarcoma can affect the conjunctiva

The following drugs have been shown to cause an increase in the level of the serum alkaline phosphatase:

- [ ] 266 nitrofurantoin
- [ ] 267 phenytoin
- [ ] 268 erythromycin
- [ ] 269 tetracycline
- [ ] 270 disulfiram

Concerning atrophic vaginitis:

- [ ] 271 it is the main reason that healthy retired couples refrain from intercourse
- [ ] 272 candida infection is the commonest cause of associated itching
- [ ] 273 local oestrogen therapy initially burns on application
- [ ] 274 prolonged local oestrogen therapy needs to be supplemented with progestogen
- [ ] 275 oestrogenic effects on the sexual partner have been reported when the spouse uses topical oestrogens

Folic acid

- ☐ 276 is found in green vegetables
- ☐ 277 is absorbed in the upper small bowel
- ☐ 278 is degraded by cooking
- ☐ 279 will reverse the macrocytosis associated with alcoholism
- ☐ 280 body stores are usually adequate for 3 years

When identifying patients with psychological problems in a consultation, research has shown general practitioners

- ☐ 281 miss many disorders
- ☐ 282 vary nine fold in their diagnosis of psychological problems
- ☐ 283 who show more empathy detect more problems
- ☐ 284 who make eye contact detect more problems
- ☐ 285 who are good at dealing with interruptions to the consultation detect less problems

Absorption of the following drugs has been shown to be increased if they are given on an empty stomach:

- ☐ 286 digoxin
- ☐ 287 allopurinol
- ☐ 288 cotrimoxazole
- ☐ 289 theophylline
- ☐ 290 penicillin

When considering treatment for prostatic carcinoma

- ☐ 291 gonadotrophin releasing analogues have been shown to be as effective as bilateral orchidectomy
- ☐ 292 asymptomatic, microscopically detected disease has been shown not to need treatment
- ☐ 293 stiboesterol administration is associated with an increase in deaths from cardiovascular disease
- ☐ 294 androgen receptor blockers are associated with an increase in metastatic bone pain in the first week of treatment
- ☐ 295 gonadotrophin releasing analogues are associated with gynaecomastia

Concerning jaundice in the neonate:

☐ 296 approximately half of all children are visibly icteric in the first week of life

☐ 297 physiological jaundice typically reaches peak levels at the 4th day

☐ 298 occurring on the first day of life is typically physiological

☐ 299 it is associated with hypothyroidism

☐ 300 it is associated with urinary tract infection

A recently born baby has been diagnosed as having a hemiplegia due to cerebral palsy. When counselling the parents subseqently the doctor should be aware that

☐ 301 the mean I.Q. is about 80

☐ 302 the majority of children have speech problems

☐ 303 the incidence of specific learning defects has been shown to be greater than for the general population

☐ 304 those with persistent hypotonia have a better prognosis than those who develop spasticity

☐ 305 for children with an I.Q. greater than 70, education should be in the normal system

In stress polycythemia

☐ 306 the PCV is typically greater than 0.55

☐ 307 the total body red cell mass is raised

☐ 308 it is commoner in females

☐ 309 it is associated with obesity

☐ 310 it is associated with excessive alcohol consumption

When counselling a couple with involuntary infertility, the following are true:

- ☐ 311 the commonest reason for the problem is an abnormality of the Fallopian tubes
- ☐ 312 the majority of couples not using contraceptives will conceive within 12 months
- ☐ 313 reconstructive tubal surgery carries an increased risk of ectopic pregnancy
- ☐ 314 the majority of women receiving clomiphene for anovulation will still not ovulate
- ☐ 315 in-vitro fertilisation is associated with an increased incidence of fetal abnormalities

Psychogenic hyperventilation is associated with

- ☐ 316 alkalosis
- ☐ 317 a decreased peak expiratory flow rate
- ☐ 318 paraesthesia of the hands
- ☐ 319 cyanosis

When updating practice premises under the Cost Rent Scheme

- ☐ 320 the final amount paid depends upon the district valuers assessment of the overall value of the completed project
- ☐ 321 the practice has to pay the capital
- ☐ 322 the FHSA will reimburse interest on the loan
- ☐ 323 payment begins as soon as the building work has commenced
- ☐ 324 it is only available for building new premises

Following a bereavement it has been shown that

- ☐ 325 approximately 20% of widowers die in the first year
- ☐ 326 mortality is greater for men than for women
- ☐ 327 mortality is still greater than expected at 2 years post bereavement

A 42 year old man presents with a depressive illness, the following factors would support an unfavourable prognosis:

☐ 328 loss of mother prior to 12 years of age
☐ 329 previous depressive illness
☐ 330 involvement with local charitable organisations
☐ 331 obsessional personality
☐ 332 a wife house bound with multiple sclerosis

When initiating treatment with a progestogen only contraceptive, the following points are true:

☐ 333 extra contraceptive precautions should be used if started on day 1 of the cycle
☐ 334 they should not be taken for 4 weeks prior to surgery
☐ 335 if switching from a combined oral contraceptive, they should be commenced after the 7 day break
☐ 336 post abortion they should be started on the day after the operation
☐ 337 they are secreted in significant amounts in breast milk

A 13 year old boy attends the surgery without an adult accompanying him, he has a sore throat. Legally a general practitioner must

☐ 338 examine and prescribe as appropriate
☐ 339 refuse to see him unless a responsible adult is present
☐ 340 write to the parent asking them to come to the surgery
☐ 341 examine but not prescribe

Concerning postgraduate education allowance (PGEA):

☐ 342 part time principals are not allowed to claim the full allowance
☐ 343 more than 10 days education in any one year cannot be counted
☐ 344 distance learning courses are not eligible
☐ 345 vocational training in the previous 12 months qualifies a newly registered principal for the full allowance

When considering whether to give a patient with a sore throat antibiotics, the following are true:

☐ 346　approximately 30% of throat swabs grow beta haemolytic streptococcus

☐ 347　about 20% of throat swabs grow *Haemophilus influenza*

☐ 348　the decrease in the incidence of rheumatic fever commenced at the time of the introduction of antibiotics

☐ 349　tonsillar exudate in an under 15 year old is typically associated with glandular fever

☐ 350　enlarged tonsillar glands are typically associated with bacterial infection

When advising patients about exposure to sun, the following are true:

☐ 351　solar keratoses never progress to malignancy

☐ 352　solar keratoses are commoner in fair skinned people

☐ 353　chronic sun exposure leads to loss of skin elasticity

☐ 354　basal cell carcinoma never metastasize

☐ 355　sunburn typically develops within 2 hours of exposure

Owning dogs has been shown to be associated with

☐ 356　a decrease in presentation of minor health problems to the general practitioner

☐ 357　an increase in one year survival following a myocardial infarction

☐ 358　a lower blood pressure when matched with the average population

☐ 359　lower lipid levels when matched with the average population

☐ 360　increase in gastrointestinal infections

MCQ PRACTICE PAPER 5

360 Questions : time allowed 2 hours.

Allergic conjunctivitis is associated with

- ☐ 1 a mucopurulent ocular discharge
- ☐ 2 a reduction in visual acuity
- ☐ 3 photophobia
- ☐ 4 epiphora
- ☐ 5 a need to avoid contact lenses

When considering alcohol dependency in women, the followimg are true:

- ☐ 6 alcohol dependent women are more prone to cerebral damage than men
- ☐ 7 alcoholic cirrhosis has a greater prevalence in women
- ☐ 8 affective disorders have been shown to be more common in male rather than female alcoholics
- ☐ 9 vulnerability to intoxication is dependent on the stage of the menstrual cycle
- ☐ 10 typically women begin drinking heavily earlier than their male counterparts

A prescription issued for a controlled drug must comply with the following:

- ☐ 11 it cannot be issued on a computer generated script
- ☐ 12 the address of the doctor must be handwritten
- ☐ 13 the script must be marked with C.D. by the issuing doctor
- ☐ 14 the total quantity of the drugs must be given in words and figures
- ☐ 15 the frequency with which the drug is to be taken must be given in words and figures

When considering a diagnosis of diabetes mellitus

- ☐ 16 blood glucose progressively rises with age
- ☐ 17 the majority of people with glycosuria have diabetes
- ☐ 18 routine urine testing detects the majority of previously undiagnosed diabetics
- ☐ 19 a fasting blood glucose of greater than 7.2 mmol/l is diagnostic of diabetes
- ☐ 20 the majority of diabetics will have retinal changes at diagnosis

A 50 year old man presents with pain in the left ear, on examination the ear appears to be normal. The following could account for the pain:

- ☐ 21 arthritis of C2-C3 level of the cervical spine
- ☐ 22 carcinoma of the pyriform fossa
- ☐ 23 impacted wisdom teeth
- ☐ 24 trigeminal neuralgia
- ☐ 25 tonsillitis

Chronic schizophrenia is characterised by the following:

- ☐ 26 apathy
- ☐ 27 slowness
- ☐ 28 somatic hallucinations
- ☐ 29 social withdrawal
- ☐ 30 depressive symptoms

Under the theoretical model of the consultation proposed by Stott and Davies the following aspects of a consultation are considered:

- ☐ 31 prevention
- ☐ 32 patients expectations
- ☐ 33 management of continuing problems
- ☐ 34 modification of health seeking behaviour
- ☐ 35 sharing of the problem with the patient

A 45 year old patient presents with chest pain, the following are more typically associated with a non cardiac origin of the pain:

- ☐ 36 breathlessness on trivial effort
- ☐ 37 palpitations
- ☐ 38 exhaustion persisting during rest
- ☐ 39 lightheadedness
- ☐ 40 headache

When considering a diagnosis of dermatofibroma, the lesions

- ☐ 41 are commoner in women
- ☐ 42 are typically pigmented
- ☐ 43 have malignant potential
- ☐ 44 typically ulcerate centrally
- ☐ 45 have an irregular edge

Concerning Hepatitis B vaccine

- ☐ 46 seroconversion is age dependent
- ☐ 47 the preferred site of injection for maximal absorption is the buttock
- ☐ 48 hypersensitivity reactions occur in more than 5% of patients
- ☐ 49 local soreness occurs in less than 10% of injections
- ☐ 50 the genetic recombinant vaccine also protects against hepatitis C

Psoriasis

- ☐ 51 will affect approximately 2 in every 100 patients
- ☐ 52 tends to leave scars
- ☐ 53 typically is itchy
- ☐ 54 on the face can be treated safely with dithranol
- ☐ 55 is typically symmetrical
- ☐ 56 usually begins between the ages of 15-25 years

When considering a protocol for the management of epilepsy within your practice

- ☐ 57 patients should be referred to a neurologist only after a second fit
- ☐ 58 if a first fit occurs after the age of 30 years of age, idiopathic epilepsy is the probable diagnosis
- ☐ 59 the majority of epileptics have an inherited condition
- ☐ 60 the majority of GPs will be aware of all the epileptics on their lists
- ☐ 61 the majority of epileptics receive an annual check from either their GP or consultant

Concerning prescription analysis and cost reports (PACT)

☐ 62 they are only available on request
☐ 63 level 3 reports can be requested for an individual therapeutic group
☐ 64 an allowance is made for the increased prescribing needs of patients over 65 years of age
☐ 65 the prescription pricing authority data has an accepted inherent inaccuracy of about 5%
☐ 66 data is based on what the GP prescribes rather than what the chemist dispenses

Pregnant women should be advised to avoid

☐ 67 prepacked salad and coleslaw
☐ 68 paté
☐ 69 unwashed fruit
☐ 70 aerobics
☐ 71 emptying cat litter trays

A 19 year old student presents with bloody diarrhoea two weeks after completing a back packing holiday in east Africa. The following should be included in a differential diagnosis:

☐ 72 typhoid fever
☐ 73 amoebic dysentery
☐ 74 schistosomiasis
☐ 75 Lassa fever
☐ 76 malaria

When considering a diagnosis of post traumatic stress disorder

☐ 77 it typically commences within one week of the event
☐ 78 the majority of those exposed to a disaster will suffer chronic symptoms
☐ 79 feelings of unreality occur
☐ 80 guilt feelings are typical
☐ 81 recovery is hindered by being pressed to talk about the event in the early stages

Urgent referral to an ophthalmologist is indicated for the following:

- ☐ 82 episcleritis
- ☐ 83 herpes zoster with visual disturbance
- ☐ 84 blocked naso-lacrimal duct at 6 months of age
- ☐ 85 a dendritic ulcer
- ☐ 86 a corneal abrasion

A 2 year old child becomes acutely ill. The following would support a diagnosis of Reye's syndrome:

- ☐ 87 chicken pox 10 days previously
- ☐ 88 behaviour changes
- ☐ 89 profuse vomiting
- ☐ 90 normal liver function tests
- ☐ 91 recent administration of aspirin

When considering the care of patients in community hospitals

- ☐ 92 the majority of GPs have access to such hospitals
- ☐ 93 the average age of patients in these hospitals is over 70 years of age
- ☐ 94 the average cost of an inpatient admission is greater than for a general hospital
- ☐ 95 the workload of GPs with access to community hospitals is greater
- ☐ 96 the majority of patients are discharged to their own homes

Synergism has been shown to occur between the following pairs of drugs:

- ☐ 97 propranolol and nifedipine
- ☐ 98 bendrofluazide and glibenclamide
- ☐ 99 spironolactone and frusemide
- ☐ 100 ibuprofen and warfarin
- ☐ 101 ethanol and chlorpheniramine

When advising a patient about hysteroscopic endometrial ablation the following are true:

☐ 102 danazol is given pre operatively
☐ 103 it is unsuitable in patients with previously treated CIN
☐ 104 the healing process takes 3 months
☐ 105 it is suitable for day case surgery
☐ 106 subsequent scanty bleeding would be an indication of treatment failure

When considering lesions of the Achilles tendon

☐ 107 tendonitis is associated with a raised heel tab on the shoe
☐ 108 local steroid injections are associated with rupture of the tendon
☐ 109 complete rupture is best treated by surgery
☐ 110 shoe raise typically leads to shortening of the tendon if used to treat Achilles tendonitis
☐ 111 ultrasound treatment leads to a worsening of the pain

The following would suggest that a patient who is HIV positive has developed 'full blown' AIDS:

☐ 112 persistent generalised lymphadenopathy
☐ 113 night sweats
☐ 114 non-Hodgkin's lymphoma
☐ 115 fatigue
☐ 116 weight loss

A 4 year old boy is noted to have a cardiac murmur on routine examination, the following would indicate its innocent nature:

☐ 117 diastolic in timing
☐ 118 murmur louder on deep inspiration
☐ 119 short duration
☐ 120 soft murmur
☐ 121 a normal chest X-ray

Central features of manic disorders are

- ☐ 122 decreased libido
- ☐ 123 expansive ideas
- ☐ 124 decreased appetite
- ☐ 125 reduced sleep
- ☐ 126 retained insight

Carcinoma of the bronchus is associated with exposure to the following:

- ☐ 127 asbestos
- ☐ 128 silica dust
- ☐ 129 sulphur dioxide
- ☐ 130 aniline dyes
- ☐ 131 radon gas

The following would support a diagnosis of Ménière's disease:

- ☐ 132 tinnitus
- ☐ 133 a feeling of fullness in the ear
- ☐ 134 fluctuating sensorineural hearing loss
- ☐ 135 a positive Romberg's test
- ☐ 136 nystagmus occurring between acute attacks

An incidental finding of an easily palpable firm spleen is most likely due to

- ☐ 137 glandular fever
- ☐ 138 carcinomatosis
- ☐ 139 chronic myeloid leukaemia
- ☐ 140 lymphoma
- ☐ 141 myelosclerosis

Under the Abortion Act 1967, when a termination of pregnancy is to be performed, the following should be considered:

☐ 142 if the patient is married the consent of the husband is necessary
☐ 143 those under 16 years of age must have the consent of a parent
☐ 144 in an emergency situation only one practitioner need sign a recommendation
☐ 145 all operations are notified to the Department of Health
☐ 146 the Act does not apply in Northern Ireland

When considering health promotion banding payments

☐ 147 a practice running a diabetic clinic will receive band 1 payments
☐ 148 fees are independent of list size
☐ 149 band 2 payments require a practice to maintain a register of patients with strokes
☐ 150 band 3 requires the body mass index to be calculated on patients
☐ 151 payments for clinics which existed prior to the introduction of the scheme continue

A elderly patient with previously stable anticoagulation treatment suddenly becomes unstable, the following causes should be considered:

☐ 152 alcoholism
☐ 153 cardiac failure
☐ 154 concurrent administration of cimetidine
☐ 155 malnutrition
☐ 156 concurrent administration of allopurinol

Statistically it has been shown that cigarette smoking decreases the incidence of the following diseases:

☐ 157 farmer's lung
☐ 158 Parkinson's disease
☐ 159 endometrial cancer
☐ 160 ulcerative colitis
☐ 161 Alzheimer's disease

Concerning carcinoma of the oesophagus:

☐ 162 the incidence is decreasing
☐ 163 adenocarcinoma have a better prognosis than squamous carcinoma
☐ 164 it is associated with coeliac disease
☐ 165 it typically presents with weight loss
☐ 166 it is a complication of achalasia

When considering the psychological aspects of pain

☐ 167 approximately 25% of patients with chronic pain will show significant response to a placebo
☐ 168 introverts seek pain relief sooner than extroverts
☐ 169 complaints of pain are more common in the elderly
☐ 170 pain perception is increased by social isolation

The following drugs can be successfully administered via a nebuliser:

☐ 171 terbutaline
☐ 172 sodium cromoglycate
☐ 173 theophylline
☐ 174 ipatropium bromide
☐ 175 beclomethasone

When considering diverticular disease

☐ 176 diverticuli are seen more frequently in the distal colon
☐ 177 non fermentable fibre is more effective than fermentable fibre in treatment
☐ 178 it has an increased incidence of carcinoma of the colon
☐ 179 bleeding is indicative of developing malignancy
☐ 180 pneumaturia is a rare complication

When applying for an order under the Mental Health Act

- ☐ 181 the nearest relative must be a first degree relative
- ☐ 182 the majority of admissions under the Act from general practitioners are made under Section 4
- ☐ 183 doctors are at greater legal risk from failing to use the Act than from over zealous use
- ☐ 184 psychiatric community nurses can make an application for admission
- ☐ 185 sexual deviancy, in itself, is a justification for compulsory admission

Concerning nitrate tolerance:

- ☐ 186 tolerance to the adverse effects, such as headache, indicate tolerance to the therapeutic effects
- ☐ 187 it typically takes at least one month to develop
- ☐ 188 topical nitrates have been shown not to produce tolerance
- ☐ 189 isosorbide mononitrate has been shown not to produce tolerance
- ☐ 190 once tolerance has developed it is permanent

In epididymitis

- ☐ 191 it has a peak incidence between 12-18 years of age
- ☐ 192 iliac fossa pain is typical
- ☐ 193 the scrotal contents remain normal in size
- ☐ 194 ultrasound scanning is diagnostic
- ☐ 195 it is associated with chlamydial infection

A 78 year old resident of a residential home becomes increasingly agitated. The following may account for this:

- ☐ 196 recent introduction of digoxin
- ☐ 197 paracetamol being given for osteoarthritis
- ☐ 198 temazepam as a hypnotic that has been given for the last 5 years
- ☐ 199 a silent myocardial infarction
- ☐ 200 dehydration

The following are true of a 'frozen shoulder':

- ☐ 201 recovery is usually complete
- ☐ 202 painful arc is typical of rotator cuff lesions
- ☐ 203 local tenderness bears no relationship to the site of the lesion
- ☐ 204 immobilisation is the treatment of choice
- ☐ 205 the pain is typically worse during the night

A young adult patient presents with dyspnoea, a chest X-ray shows hilar lymphadenopathy, the following are possible causes:

- ☐ 206 streptococcal pneumonia
- ☐ 207 sarcoidosis
- ☐ 208 lymphoma
- ☐ 209 tuberculosis
- ☐ 210 pulmonary rheumatoid disease

Concerning cervical smears:

- ☐ 211 atypia on a single occasion correlates well with the presence of CIN
- ☐ 212 the majority of carcinomas of the cervix are diagnosed from cervical smears
- ☐ 213 if there is a history of genital warts a smear should be undertaken annually
- ☐ 214 cervical erosions typically produce an abnormal cervical smear
- ☐ 215 once fixed a cervical smear must reach the laboratory within 48 hours to allow accurate interpretation

The following would support a diagnosis of irritant contact dermatitis:

- ☐ 216 severity that varies with the amount of exposure to the irritant
- ☐ 217 rash developing two days after exposure
- ☐ 218 reactivation of a rash in other sites
- ☐ 219 positive patch tests
- ☐ 220 no previous exposure to the suspected irritant

Concerning Paget's disease:

☐ 221 patients have been shown to become refractory to calcitonin therapy
☐ 222 deafness is a complication
☐ 223 cardiac failure is a complication
☐ 224 hypercalcaemia is typical
☐ 225 a normal alkaline phosphatase excludes the diagnosis

Toddler diarrhoea is characterised by the following:

☐ 226 typically occurs after an acute infection
☐ 227 is associated with failure to thrive
☐ 228 trial of a milk free diet has been shown to be beneficial
☐ 229 presence of undigested food in the stools
☐ 230 response to loperamide

Concerning benzodiazepine dependence:

☐ 231 the majority of patients taking a benzodiazepine regularly for six months or more will suffer a withdrawal reaction on stopping the drug
☐ 232 dependence has been shown to occur after 3 weeks of treatment
☐ 233 a characteristic feature of withdrawal is loss of appetite
☐ 234 auditory hallucinations would indicate other psychopathology
☐ 235 beta-blockers have been shown to attenuate the withdrawal symptoms

When reading scientific papers

☐ 236 significance levels are greater the higher the value of p
☐ 237 accepting the Null hypothesis means that there is significant difference
☐ 238 Student's 't' test is used for significance testing on large samples
☐ 239 Spearman's rank correlation applies to results in a single group
☐ 240 standard deviation measures the variation about the mean

The following are true of vaginal contraceptive diaphragms:

☐ 241 they should be removed within 2 hours of intercourse
☐ 242 the size may need to be changed if the patients weight varies by more than 7 lbs
☐ 243 they can be used if utero-vaginal prolapse is present
☐ 244 they need to be renewed annually
☐ 245 they can be used if the patient is allergic to rubber

When treating vomiting symptomatically

☐ 246 hyoscine is available as a skin patch
☐ 247 domperidone is licensed as an injection
☐ 248 cinnarazine is available without a prescription
☐ 249 procloperazine is associated with postural hypotension
☐ 250 chlorpromazine is as effective as prochloperazine

Febrile convulsions

☐ 251 typically occur in the second year of life
☐ 252 are commoner in social class V
☐ 253 are commoner in boys rather than girls
☐ 254 with complex fits lasting longer than 15 minutes have been shown to be associated with epilepsy in later life
☐ 255 show a familial incidence

Concerning varicose veins:

☐ 256 sclerotherapy cures less than 10% over a 5 year period
☐ 257 ligation of the long saphenous vein is more complex than the short saphenous vein
☐ 258 after multiple avulsions compression is necessary for an average of one month
☐ 259 walking distances should be delayed until one week after surgery
☐ 260 the average patient with uncomplicated surgery for veins in one leg will require 6 weeks away from work

During pregnancy the following chronic diseases typically deteriorate:

- ☐ 261 epilepsy
- ☐ 262 migraine
- ☐ 263 multiple sclerosis
- ☐ 264 asthma
- ☐ 265 sickle cell disease

The following statements are true about eye drops:

- ☐ 266 fluorsecein stains soft contact lenses
- ☐ 267 pilocarpine causes pupillary dilatation
- ☐ 268 benoxinate causes pain when instilled into a normal eye
- ☐ 269 tropicamide anaesthetises the cornea
- ☐ 270 adrenalin produces local irritation

In Guillian-Barre syndrome

- ☐ 271 there is typically an antecedent 'viral' infection
- ☐ 272 sensory symptoms predominate over motor symptoms
- ☐ 273 it typically develops insidiously
- ☐ 274 the majority of cases recover
- ☐ 275 the central nervous system is typically spared

Concerning diabetic pregnancies:

- ☐ 276 congenital abnormalities are more common
- ☐ 277 pre-term labour is increased in frequency
- ☐ 278 uncomplicated pregnancies are usually induced at 40 weeks gestation
- ☐ 279 neonatal jaundice is increased in the offspring
- ☐ 280 epidural analgesia is contraindicated in diabetics

A 6 year old boy presents with a limp and pain in the hip, the following differential diagnoses should be considered:

- ☐ 281 tuberculosis of the hip
- ☐ 282 Perthe's disease
- ☐ 283 slipped upper femoral epiphysis
- ☐ 284 septic arthritis
- ☐ 285 non accidental injury

In considering the diagnosis of erythema mutiforme

- ☐ 286 it typically occurs without any discernible precipitating cause
- ☐ 287 the rash is not characteristic
- ☐ 288 if mucous membranes are involved carries a worse prognosis
- ☐ 289 recurrent episodes are extremely rare
- ☐ 290 it typically resolves after approximately 10 days

The following are true about cholesterol:

- ☐ 291 a raised cholesterol has been shown to be a risk factor for coronary artery disease
- ☐ 292 decreasing cholesterol has been shown to decrease overall mortality
- ☐ 293 a low cholesterol has a significant association with carcinoma
- ☐ 294 good dietary control will reduce cholesterol levels by about 30%
- ☐ 295 those who smoke should not be screened

Aspirin

- ☐ 296 has been shown to reduce the incidence of cataracts
- ☐ 297 reduces the mortality if given after a myocardial infarction
- ☐ 298 in low dose is associated with a risk of retinal haemorrhage
- ☐ 299 is effective in the treatment of venous thromboembolism
- ☐ 300 has been shown to have a role in the primary prevention of cerebrovascular disease

Child physical abuse is associated with an increased incidence in

☐ 301 females
☐ 302 illegitimate children
☐ 303 those of low birthweight
☐ 304 those under 3 years of age

Excessive hair loss is associated with

☐ 305 seborrhoeic eczema
☐ 306 tinea capitis
☐ 307 minoxidil treatment
☐ 308 hormone replacement therapy
☐ 309 hirsutism

The following would indicate a diagnosis of stress incontinence in female patients:

☐ 310 nocturia occurring three times nightly
☐ 311 dribbling after passing water
☐ 312 leaking small amounts of urine
☐ 313 having to 'rush' to get to the toilet on time

The 'Red Book', (Statement of fees and allowances)

☐ 314 is a legally binding document
☐ 315 can only be amended by legislative change
☐ 316 is negotiated by the LMC on behalf of all general practitioners

Disability living allowance

☐ 317 is only available to people whose disability arises after the age of 65 years of age
☐ 318 is paid in addition to the mobility allowance if eligible
☐ 319 is paid after a qualifying period of 3 months
☐ 320 is a tax free benefit

The following are true of premenstrual syndrome:

☐ 321 caffeine restriction has been shown to decrease symptoms
☐ 322 fertility is decreased in those who suffer from severe symptoms
☐ 323 the majority of women seek help from their doctor with symptoms related to the condition
☐ 324 suppression of ovulation typically relieves symptoms

Immediate hospital referral is indicated in a three year old child who ingests one of the following:

☐ 325 10 tablets of penicillin V 250 mg
☐ 326 10 tablets of the combined oral contraceptive
☐ 327 10 quinine sulphate tablets
☐ 328 mercury from a thermometer
☐ 329 20 ml of houseplant food

When considering the nutritional values of equivalent amounts of foods, the following are true:

☐ 330 grapefruit contains more fibre than banana
☐ 331 corn flakes contain more iron than spinach
☐ 332 rye crispbread is more calorific than wholemeal bread
☐ 333 green peppers are a rich source of vitamin C
☐ 334 dry red wine contains significantly more calories than dry white wine
☐ 335 beer is a good source of vitamin B

Accidental carbon monoxide poisoning

☑ 336 is the commonest cause of death by poisoning in children
☑ 337 initial symptoms are characterised by headache
☑ 338 mental lethargy is typical
☑ 339 effects are typically reversed within 24 hours upon removal from the source
☐ 340 cyanosis occurs in the later stages

You are investigating a couple for involuntary infertility and the sperm count of the husband is returned showing azoospermia. The following are true:

341 the condition is strongly related to mumps orchitis

342 if due to Klinefelter's syndrome, FSH levels will be raised

343 in the majority of cases there is no pathological cause detected despite full investigation

344 endocrine treatment will achieve a viable sperm count in more than 29% of cases

345 intercourse the night prior to collecting the sample has been shown to produce a temporary azoospermia

Oral decongestants used for the treatment of common colds, are contra-indicated in a patient

346 taking beta blockers

347 who discontinued mono amine oxidase inhibitors one week previously

348 who is hypothyroid

349 who is diabetic

350 who is taking non steroidal anti-inflammatory drugs

When considering tuberculosis in the United Kingdom

351 notifications of the disease are increasing

352 the majority of isolates are now resistant to isoniazid

353 trials conducted in the British Isles have failed to show the effectiveness of BCG vaccination

354 is significantly associated with the homeless population

355 about 30% of patients with AIDS will develop tuberculosis

Studies published in the United Kingdom have shown a significant association between low blood pressure and

356 tiredness

357 minor psychological symptoms

358 dizziness

359 raised serum cholesterol levels

360 a decrease in the patients perceived feeling of well-being

MCQ PAPER 1

1:True 2:False 3:False 4:True 5:True

80% of thyrotoxic patients have Graves' disease with positive thyroid antibodies. A raised TSH in a thyrotoxic patient would indicate a rare TSH-secreting tumour of the pituitary. Blocking all thyroid function with anti-thyroid drugs such as carbimazole and then replacing with thyroid hormone is the treatment of choice for Graves' disease. Thyroid adenoma is best treated surgically.

Graves' ophthalmopathy is more common in smokers and people who have had recent radio-iodine treatment. Post partum thyroiditis is common occuring in 5% of pregnancies often requiring no treatment, as it is frequently a minor disturbance.

6:False 7:False 8:False 9:False 10:True

The regulations with regard to practice leaflets have to be carefully adhered to. The age does not have to be stated but the sex of the doctor does! The date of first registration of the practice nurse does not but that of the doctor needs to be stated.

Fees charged are of no concern to the FHSA. Computerisation is often stated on leaflets but is not a requirement. However the facilities for the disabled must be stated as must the means by which people may comment on the service available.

11:True 12:True 13:True 14:True 15:True

Clomipramine tends to cause erectile dysfunction and delayed ejaculation, in low dosage it is used for the treatment of premature ejaculation.

Beta-blockers are associated with reduced sexual interest and erectile dysfunction as is chlorpromazine.

Indomethacin reduces sexual interest, corticosteroids also do this and additionally cause delay in ejaculation.

16:True 17:False 18:False 19:False 20:True

Basal cell carcinoma is the commonest skin malignancy. Although due to exposure to ultra-violet light, it rarely appears on the bald scalp, ears, lower lips, or back of the hands. It typically starts as a small pink or pearly papule.

Eventually the centre breaks down forming the ulcer which may become crusted.

It is commoner in those with freckles, red hair and blue eyes.

21:False 22:False 23:True 24:True 25:False
The onset of jaundice in cirrhosis is variable, malaise and lethargy are common at the onset. Vague gastrointestinal symptoms and especially pain with tenderness over the liver are common. Spider naevi are frequent along with other symptoms of liver failure such as gynaecomastia, testicular atrophy and a loss of male hair distribution.

The prognosis is poor but is dramatically improved if alcohol can be avoided.

26:False 27:False 28:True 29:False 30:False
Primary herpetic infection in the third trimester carries a 40% risk to the fetus. There is also a risk of premature labour. Post primary infection only carries an approximately 5% risk of fetal infection. Acyclovir is not licensed for use in pregnancy but it has been used extensively with no evidence of harm to the baby. If herpes lesions are apparent at the onset of labour a caesarian section is indicated.

In pregnancy there is a decrease in cell mediated immunity and therefore the risk of infection is probably increased.

31:True 32:False 33:False 34:False 35:True
In Henoch-Schönlein purpura there is usually a preceding upper respiratory tract infection in the two weeks prior to the onset of symptoms. Arthritis only usually lasts a few days at the most a week. It most commonly affects the knees and ankles and is usually symmetrical in distribution.

Gross or microscopic haematuria occurs in 40% with most cases recovering completely and only a few going on to renal failure or nephritis.

Skin biopsy shows the characteristic changes of acute inflammatory reaction and eosinophilic infiltration.

36:False 37:False 38:True 39:True 40:False
No study has shown an improvement over placebo with diuretics or pyridoxine. Gamolenic acid produces improvement in over 50% of cases, tamoxifen 10 mg daily improves pain but this is not covered in the product licence. HRT and the combined oral contraceptive make pain worse because of the oestrogenic drive.

41:False 42:True 43:True 44:False 45:False
The only two of these that are so called 'First Rank' symptoms are thought insertion and auditory hallucinations commenting on the patients appearance or actions. Visual hallucinations and paranoid delusions may occur but are not diagnostic. Ideas of reference can occur in other disorders.

46:True 47:True 48:False 49:False 50:True
A fee is payable for notification of a variety of diseases but the rate of reporting still under-represents the true incidence of the diseases. AIDS is not notifiable but a central register is kept of all patients with the disease which relies on voluntary reporting.

51:True 52:True 53:True 54:True 55:True
Aphthous ulcers are small round ulcers with a red margin which heal within 10 days. Lichen planus typically lasts weeks or months, the base is indurated.

A recent article has associated lichen planus with the use of NSAIDs. Primary syphilitic ulcers are painless round and have an indurated base.

Agranulocytosis may be the first manifestation of leukaemia or a side effect of drug therapy.

Behçet's disease is rare, usually affects young men and is associated with arthritis, iritis and recurrent oral and genital ulceration.

56:True 57:True 58:False 59:False 60:False
Section 47 of the National Assistance Act allows an application to be made by a community physician supported by another doctor to make an application to a magistrates court.

The supporting doctor is usually the patients GP. Once the section is approved the individual may be removed immediately, for an initial period of three weeks. The patient must not be treated without informed consent if the admission is to a hospital. Most patients are over 65 years of age and are usually women.

61:False 62:True 63:False 64:False 65:False
Eating disorders produce definite symptoms. There are certain features which would suggest an organic disorder. A loss of pubic hair would indicate hypopituitarism. LH levels are typically low in eating disorders. The ESR is normal and cortisol levels are usually high, normal or above normal, possibly related to an associated depression.

If the eating disorder has started before puberty gonadotrophin release will be delayed and therefore amenorrhoea will be primary.

66:False 67:True 68:False 69:False 70:True
An IUCD is an effective method for 5 days after coitus. The morning after pill is only effective for 3 days. There is no teratogenic risk to the fetus and it is not contraindicated when breast feeding. Mastalgia is in fact a side effect in the non pregnant woman. Because 50% of the female population is unaware of these methods they have failed to reduce unplanned pregnancies.

71:True 72:False 73:True 74:False 75:False
Pain is usually accompanied by vomiting. It is common to pass flatus or faeces after the onset of the pain. However if the obstruction is in the descending or sigmoid colon distension may be very marked before vomiting commences.

Visible peristalsis is not reliable, it is a normal finding in thin individuals with lax muscles. Bowel sounds are characteristically tinkling.

76:False 77:True 78:False 79:False 80:False
It is possible for viral infections to behave in this way. Asthma is the commonest missed diagnosis and a trial of bronchodilators is always worthwhile. Pertussis, after 5 weeks will probably have started to resolve slowly, it will have been accompanied by malaise and probably vomiting accompanying the cough. Inhaled foreign bodies will produce signs in the chest and be accompanied by tachycardia and malaise by 5 weeks.

Antibiotics are rarely justified, but often given on a 'blind' basis.

81:True 82:True 83:False 84:False 85:False
Of patients with osteoarthritis 40% have a first degree relative affected. The knee is the most commonly affected joint and is made worse by obesity. There is little correlation between X-ray appearances and the clinical condition. Activities such as swimming should be encouraged, low impact sporting activities should be gradually increased.

86:False 87:False 88:True 89:False 90:False
A bilateral progressive sensorineural loss can be induced by noise exposure.

Generally there is sparing of low frequencies and also very high frequency sounds. Excessive noise damages the hair cells of the Organ of Corti.

Recruitment (sudden amplification of the sound) is common as it is in presbyacussis. Hearing aids are particularly effective. The hearing loss is typically insidious progressing over a long period of time.

91:False 92:False 93:False 94:True 95:False
10% of shiftworkers like nightwork, 20% hate it, and the rest tolerate it.

There is no increased cardiovascular mortality but peptic ulceration is much commoner due to irregular diet, poor meals, chronic fatigue, excessive smoking and alcohol. Mental symptoms are not increased and the rate of industrial accidents is not increased.

96:True 97:True 98:True 99:True 100:False
Solvent abuse is usually a group activity of boys between 11-16 years of age.

Surveys show that it is a transient form of experimentation with 75% stopping abuse within 6 months. Acute effects include visual hallucinations, impaired judgement, slurred speech and dizziness. Chronic effects are cerebellar signs with cerebral ventricular enlargement and sometimes peripheral neuropathy. Death is not due to toluene but is due to freons.

101:True 102:True 103:True 104:True 105:True
75% of children will be dry by the time they reach 3 years of age. Daytime wetting is associated with the various cause of detrusor instability, neurological disorders or anatomical abnormalities. Pad and buzzer alarms have been shown to be most effective in those patients who have insight into their problems and actively want to have an aid to help keep them dry. Lifting

the child at night repeatedly although very effective can be very wearing on the parents. Restricting fluids has not been shown to be of any value.

106:False 107:True 108:False 109:False 110:True
The confusing range of what is and is not available on prescription is illustrated by this range of items for just one condition — diabetes.

111:True 112:False 113:True 114:False 115:True
Too rapid a reduction in steroid treatment can lead to severe symptoms such as hypotension, acute adrenal insufficiency and death. More minor symptoms such as conjunctivitis, rhinitis, malaise, arthralgia but not arthritis, loss of weight and painful itchy skin nodules are more common and their true cause may go unrecognised.

116:True 117:False 118:True 119:False 120:True
Night visit fees are complex!

Higher rates are paid for visits done by non commercial rotas between GPs.

Requests for visits must be received and the visit made between the hours of 22.00 and 08.00. Patients can be seen at home, in the surgery, or in a community hospital. In the case of the latter the fee is only payable if the doctor makes the arrangements with the patient and the hospital does not call the doctor out at night.

121:True 122:True 123:True 124:True
Although the incidence is falling in men it is rising in women. Great Britain still has the highest incidence in the world reflecting high smoking rates, poor management of industrial waste and a readiness of doctors in this country to make the diagnosis. It accounts for more days away from work than any other illness including back pain and is associated with living in an urban industrial environment.

125:False 126:False 127:True 128:False 129:True
Tinnitus is typically associated with sensorineural deafness but conductive deafness can lead to an awareness of sounds generated within the body, such as from a carotid bruit.

Treatment is often unrewarding, but treatment for depression by drugs or psychotherapy helps a proportion of patients. Surgical treatment is rarely used and the patient must be aware that the condition can be made worse by the operation.

130:True 131:False 132:True 133:True 134:False
It is virtually impossible to distinguish clinically between gastric and duodenal ulceration. They have many features in common, 10% of gastric and 15% of duodenal ulcers bleed. Night pain is present in both but is more common with duodenal ulcers.

Heliobacter pylori is found in 90% of duodenal ulcers but the significance of this is controversial at present.

A familial tendency is common to both and both have a blood group association.

Patients over 40 years of age presenting for the first time with dyspepsia should be investigated because this presentation accounts for about 26% of the total number of cancers detected.

135:True 136:True 137:True 138:False 139:False
85% of carcinomas of the bladder present with an episode of haematuria. It is associated with exposure to various industrial carcinogens, the use of phenacetin and cyclophosphamide, and of course cigarette smoking. It is probably because of the latter that the incidence is rising in women.

About half the superficial lesions treated with cystodiathermy will reoccur within 2 years.

140:False 141:True 142:True 143:False 144:False
Haemorrhages, especially the more minor ones are often misdiagnosed as infarcts. This has important implications if aspirin is to be given.

A cerebral haemorrhage typically has an abrupt onset with headache, vomiting and possible neck stiffness. The patient will often remain unconscious after 24 hr and will have a raised diastolic blood pressure at this time.

145:False 146:True 147:True 148:True 149:False
10% of all new entrants to the blind register are directly due to chronic glaucoma, they are usually over 65 years of age. Myopic patients are at a greater risk than long sighted patients, who are at a greater risk of acute glaucoma. There is a very strong familial tendency and first degree relatives of those patients with glaucoma get free eye tests.

150:True 151:False 152:True 153:False 154:False
Idiopathic thrombocytopenia would be the commonest cause. Inadequate mixing can cause platelet aggregation and a falsely low count.

Polyarteritis nodosa tends to cause an eosinophilia, whereas SLE may present with a low platelet count. Viral infections are the usual cause of a neutropenia and do not typically affect platelet count.

Dipyrimadole is an anti-platelet drug but there is no significant association with thrombocytopenia.

155:True 156:True 157:True 158:False 159:True
Chest infection is common, the prognosis is worsened by coexisting heart disease. A very high or a very low white cell count is an adverse indicator of prognosis.

Confusion is often the presenting feature of an underlying pneumonic process in an elderly patient who may appear otherwise well and have a minimum of chest signs.

160:True 161:True 162:True 163:True 164:False
Cholestyramine, a bile acid sequestrant is allowed in pregnancy, breast feeding and for use in children. Fenofibrate is allowed for the latter group, experience with all the other agents is limited. Sleep disturbances with simvastatin are typically minimal. The flushing with nicotinic acid may be severe and is also associated with dermatitis. Fibrates and HMG CoA reductase inhibitors adversely affect liver enzymes.

165:True 166:True 167:True 168:True 169:False
General practitioner contracts state that the individual doctor is responsible for care at all times, even if this care is delegated to a deputising service or practice nurse. The GP is also responsible for all staff including when their family answers the telephone.

If a GP perceives the need for a drug and it is available on an NHS prescription it must be provided. A private prescription cannot be used even if the drug is cheaper to the patient privately. Of course if it is available 'over the counter' without a prescription the patient can be advised of this.

The commonest reason for a complaint against a GP is failure to visit.

170:True 171:False 172:True 173:False 174:True
Surveys have shown that 50% of women who complain that their menstrual loss is heavy have an average loss by normal criteria. Dysfunctional uterine bleeding is diagnosed when there is absence of other factors such as fibroids.

D&C is usually employed to detect an underlying endometrial carcinoma, the incidence of which in those under 40 years is 1:100,000. Younger patients would probably be better given a vabra curettage or a hysteroscopy.

Mefenamic acid has been shown to decrease blood loss by 25% and also to decrease associated pain.

175:True 176:True 177:True 178:True 179:True
Retinal detachment has a reasonable prognosis for sight if detected early. If central vision is spared, visual acuity will be normal. Black spots and floaters probably are the presenting symptom that cause the most worry to GPs as they are often associated with disturbances within the vitreous which are of little importance.

180:False 181:False 182:False 183:False 184:True
About one third of all subarachnoid haemorrhages occur in those over 65 years. The majority are due to a ruptured cerebral aneurysm, pre-existing hypertension worsens the prognosis. The most common presentation in the elderly is with confusion or coma. The mortality in this age group is greater than 50%.

185:True 186:True 187:False 188:False 189:True
The drugs quoted here join a growing list, the most important of which appears to be aspirin.

190:True 191:False 192:False 193:True 194:True
Emergency care is free to all visitors to the UK no matter which country they

come from. So is any domiciliary nursing care that is needed.

For other care reciprocal arrangements exist with many countries and their nationals can be treated under the NHS. Australia is one such country.

A fee can be charged by the first doctor who attends any person involved in a road traffic accident. The bill is usually paid by the insurance company of the vehicle involved without detriment to the driver's 'no claims bonus'.

195:True 196:False 197:False 198:True
Constitutional delay is the commonest reason and is defined as puberty delayed beyond 16 years in girls and beyond 18 years in boys. It can be regarded as a variation of normal. The bone age corresponds to the stage of development not chronological age. A raised gonadotrophin level would be indicative of perhaps Turner's syndrome, Klinefelter's or primary gonadal failure.

There is typically a family history of late puberty, so it is always worth asking the parents.

199:False 200:False 201:True 202:True 203:True 204:False
Breast feeding fails because of inadequate support and poor, inconsistent and antiquated advice from health care workers. Practices that were shown to be incorrect 30 years ago are still being taught. Initial feeds should not be time restricted they should be for as long as mother and baby feel comfortable. If sore breasts occur it is usually poor positioning of the baby not excessive sucking.

Just feeding from one breast at a particular feed is justifiable. The fat content of the milk has been shown to increase as the feed progresses.

The subsequent incidence of breast cancer in breast feeding women is not increased, various studies have shown a decrease.

205:True 206:True 207:True 208:False 209:True 210:True
When sampling populations it is essential to decrease bias. Retrospective studies are prone to bias as are subjective studies because the results are based on opinion rather than fact. Standardisation is essential between the control group and the group under investigation. Stratified sampling

compartmentalises the groups within a sample allowing less variation.

It is better to use random numbers than sampling at regular intervals. The regularity could coincide by chance with some other unforeseen regularity in the material under study.

211:True 212:True 213:True 214:False 215:False
Suicide in alcoholics is especially prevalent during relapses after a period of abstinence. If episodes of aggression are directed towards themselves they are particularly at risk. The social and psychological isolation engendered by physical illness leaves patients at an immense risk. An urban environment is more associated with suicide than a rural one. The most vulnerable people are male, older age and single, but there has been an increase recently in the incidence in younger males.

216:True 217:False 218:True 219:True 220:False
Hair loss of a diffuse nature is associated with iron deficiency in the elderly.

Conversely scalp ringworm only causes localised loss in children. Warfarin has hair loss as a reported side effect. Alopecia areata, with the typical exclamation mark hairs typically causes patchy loss but diffuse loss is known.

Trichotillomania, in which the patient deliberately pulls the hair out, produces a well defined area of hair loss. The hairs are very short rather than absent.

221:True 222:True 223:False 224:False 225:False
Ectopic pregnancy has increased by 30% in the last 20 years, possibly due to the increase in pelvic inflammatory disease. The death rate has fallen but it still accounts for 10% of maternal mortality.

If the pregnancy test is positive with low levels of HCG and the uterus is empty at 6 weeks gestation then ectopic pregnancy is likely. Ultrasound on its own is unreliable with 5-10% showing an adnexal mass with a gestational sac.

Neither the IUCD or progestogen only pill are associated with ectopic pregnancy.

226:False 227:True 228:True 229:False 230:True.
It is always worth knowing a few drugs that are safe and checking any others in the BNF.

231:False 232:True 233:False 234:False 235:True
Pompholyx is an extremely itchy variant of eczema, typically affecting soles of feet and palms of hands. The epidermal fluid of the eczematous condition is trapped in the thickened stratum and produces a 'sago' like appearance.

Strong steroids are often needed in resistant cases. It is not associated with atopy or eczema elsewhere. Mycology should be checked before starting treatment if the condition is severe.

236:False 237:True 238:False 239:False 240:True
Ovarian cancer is much commoner in nulliparous women, even a single early spontaneous abortion seems to afford some degree of protection. One year of treatment on the combined pill produces the same protection as a full term pregnancy. If a first degree relative has had the condition the risk is increased by 2-3 fold. The overall survival is 30% rising to 65% if detected at stage I. Unfortunately, the presentation is often silent, only 15-20% have abnormal bleeding The commonest presentation is abdominal pain either with or without abdominal swelling.

241:True 242:True 243:True 244:True 245:False
Cognitive behaviour therapy is in vogue at the moment, it assumes that how people perceive and structure their experiences determines how they feel and behave. Negative aspects and unadaptive patterns of thinking are concentrated on, in a number of sessions which may need to be as many as 15 at weekly intervals. It is suitable for a wide variety of psychological conditions.

246:True 247:True 248:False 249:False 250:False
Ethosuximide is used in the treatment of absence seizures, peak serum levels occur 1-4 hours after administration and the control is highly correlated with the plasma levels.

Primidone is converted to phenobarbitone at a steady rate in the ratio 1:2.5. Sodium valproate is completely absorbed from the gut after oral administration. It is highly protein bound and this makes interpretation of blood levels difficult.

Vigabactrin increases brain levels of GABA (gamma amino butyric acid) which is a powerful inhibitor of neural transmission. Plasma monitoring at present does not appear to correlate well with efficiency.

Clonazepam, tolerance develops and drug levels are therefore of no value.

251:False 252:True 253:False 254:False 255:True

Faecal occult blood testing is unacceptable to a lot of people. It has a high false positive rate of approximately 54% in one trial. Sensitivity is of the order of 75% for a 3 day test rising to 90% for a 5 day test. It is more sensitive for distal tumours. In caecal tumours, haematin released may be broken down in its passage through the remaining colon.

Certain foods such as banana, radish, broccoli, parsnip, turnip and cauliflower have peroxidase activity which can lead to false positives.

256:False 257:True 258:True 259:True 260:False

Proliferative retinopathy is seen on the optic disc but background retinopathy is first seen on the temporal side of the macula. The earliest visible changes are micro-aneurysms and haemorrhages. In the UK, diabetes is the commonest cause of blind registration between the ages of 20-65 years of age.

261:True 262:True 263:False 264:True 265:True

Breath holding attacks tend to occur in children who are easily frustrated. Recovery from an attack is rapid and there are no after effects such as drowsiness which would occur after a fit.

Cyanosis is transient and extended tonic posture and shaking or twitching might make the parents think that the child has had a convulsion.

266:False 267:True 268:False 269:True 270:True

If the femoral stretch test is positive this localises the lesion to an L2-L3 level.

Pain is felt in the muscles innervated by the damaged nerve. The spinal cord ends at L1 therefore an extensor plantar response suggests that there is some other pathology. A large central disc prolapse may compress the sacral roots in the cauda equina and cause a loss of bladder function.

271:True 272:False 273:True 274:False 275:False
Many antibiotics have been implicated in causing pseudomembranous colitis but systemic clindamycin, amoxycillin, ampicillin and the cephalosporins are the most common. The toxin of the organism *Clostridium difficile* is the causative factor. Vancomycin and metronidazole have been shown to be effective in a patient who is toxic. Blood in the stools is a rare finding usually only with the severe type of infection. The peripheral blood film shows a polymorph leucocytosis and there are leucocytes in the stools.

276:True 277:False 278:True: 279:True 280:False
Alzheimer's disease is often missed in the early stages because early symptoms such as preference for routine and mild spatial disorientation are associated with 'forgetfulness' of age. Memory loss is characteristically short term for recent events.

In the later stages loss of speech, grand mal seizures and spasticity of limbs add to the worsening mental problems.

281:False 282:True 283:False 284:False 285:True
Sulphonylureas are associated with an increase in weight, metformin is the drug of choice in the overweight diabetic if dietary measures fail. This increase in weight and the loss of effect the longer they are used is the greatest limitation to the use of sulphonylureas.

In the elderly there are probably more important problems than strict control, such as good foot care, associated hypertension and control of eye symptoms.

Clinically 20-30% will show retinopathy at the time of diagnosis, however fluorescein angiography shows that the majority have started with retinopathy.

The current view on diet is that it should be kept simple with a restriction of fat and encouragement to eat complex carbohydrates.

286:False 287:True 288:True 289:False 290:True
Care needs to be taken with prescribing for hay fever in children. Terfenadine has had its product licence modified so that it can now be used from 3 years of age upwards.

Xylometazoline can be given at a dose of 1-2 drops every 8-12 hours.

Sodium cromoglycate drops are given at a dose of 1-2 drops, 4 times daily.

291:False 292:True 293:False 294:True 295:False
Resting ECGs are of little value, ST segment and T wave changes could reflect LVH, or in inferior leads they can appear with changes in respiration and posture. The amount of ST depression at a given workload and the duration this persists after exercise is highly relevant. The normal physiological response to exercise is an increase in heart rate and a rise in systolic blood pressure. If the BP falls this indicates impaired left ventricular function due to myocardial ischaemia. Ambulatory monitoring indicates how easy it is to underestimate the problem of ischaemia. The morbidity of coronary angiography is 1:300 with a mortality rate of 1:2000.

296:False 297:True 298:True 299:True 300:False
Dupuytren's contracture is progressive fibrosis of the palmar fascia causing painless flexion. More than one finger is often affected with 65% ring, 55% little, 25% middle, 5% index and 3% thumb.

There is also a high incidence in patients with liver disease especially alcoholics. It is said to affect the white race only and is 8 times more common in men than women.

301:True 302:True 303:True 304:True 305:True
Placebos have a high response rate of the order of 30-40% in many conditions. Studies have also shown that such factors as colour and shape of the pills are important in promulgating the depth of the placebo response.

306:True 307:False 308:False 309:False 310:True
Currently in vogue is the term 'heartsink patient', they are difficult to define and are not always frequent attenders. GPs usually contain such patients within the practice and do not refer elsewhere. The average doctor has 20-30 such patients and examining their medical record folders reveals a variety of different diagnoses at each consultation. They also have significantly more psychological, social and family problems.

311:False 312:False 313:True 314:True
At birth about 4% of foreskins are retractable, at 6 months it is 20%, at one year 50%, and by 3 years it is 90%. If left untreated phimosis may ultimately

lead to problems with micturition and sexual function. Inability to clean under the foreskin is associated with stones in the preputial sac and the development of cancer of the penis. Circumcision has a low rate of complications and is reported to be the safest surgical procedure in childhood.

315:True 316:True 317:True
Health inequalities reflect social inequalities and the risks from each of these conditions are enhanced in the lower social classes:

motor vehicle accidents 2.3:1.0
pneumonia 4.8:1.0
lung cancer 3.0:1.0.

318:False 319:True 320:True 321:True 322:True
The management of glue ear is one of the main controversies in general practice/ENT. Early referral leads to unnecessary intervention and subsequent damage to eardrums which would have remained healthy.

Conservative management especially decreasing passive smoking and possibly treatment with antibiotics has much to recommend it.

323:True 324:False 325:True 326:True 327:False
100 babies with sickle cell disease are born in the UK each year. 6000 people in Britain have the disease.

Priapism can occur in any male after 5 years of age, most commonly in sexually active men and if prolonged can lead to impotence.

Fertility is normal in women but pregnancy is associated with potential serious medical and obstetric complications.

Stroke occurs in about 7% of patients and can affect any age group from 18 months onwards, it is often precipitated by dehydration or infection.

Gall stones occur in 70% of adults.

Hypersplenism occurs in infancy and is gradually replaced by a state of hyposplenism as the patients spleen becomes more damaged eventually leading to a state of 'autosplenectomy'.

a fit. Although indomethacin does potentiate alcohol, salicylates do not have this effect. Atenolol does not cross the blood-brain barrier and therefore does not interact, however propranolol has been shown to cause drowsiness, presumably because of its lipid solubility. In susceptible individuals even the newer non-sedating antihistamines can cause some sedation with alcohol. Nearly all antidepressants potentiate alcohol and affect psychomotor performance.

101:False 102:True 103:True 104:True 105:True
Lasers are being used with greater frequency in the treatment of many conditions. Acute glaucoma is treated either by iridectomy or trabeculoplasty. The distortion of senile macular degeneration caused by leaking areas on the retina are amenable to laser treatment. Radial keratotomy is used for the treatment of myopia and surgical treatment is now being replaced by laser.

106:True 107:False 108:True 109:True 110:False
1:10 mothers get a depressive illness which can be differentiated from 'maternity blues'. It may need no more than support and counselling. Various studies have shown various associations. Obvious things such as hormonal state, social class, parity, legitimacy are NOT associated.

Housing needs have been shown to be a factor in one survey. Maternal deprivation as a child, previous psychiatric illness and ambivalence or anxiety about the pregnancy have all appeared as risk factors.

111:True 112:True 113:True 114:False 115:True
Cancer of the cervix can occur at any age from 20-90, the majority of cases occur in the 40-55 age group. Risk factors also include high parity, early pregnancy and lack of participation in screening. 55% of patients will survive more than 5 years and 47% more than 10 years.

116:True 117:False 118:True 119:True 120:False
Although this is the accepted definition the response of patients is very individual.

Catecholamines, such as adrenalin, increase blood sugars and the outpouring of adrenalin at the onset of a hypoglycaemic episode accounts for symptoms such as pallor, feeling of hunger, tachycardia, trembling and sweating. The main causes of hypoglycaemia in a previously stable diabetic are diet, exercise, infection and alcohol ingestion.

121:False 122:False 123:False 124:False 125:False
Squamous cell carcinoma appears on the helix, rodent ulcers on the skin behind and below the ear. Tophi appear on the antihelix. Psoriasis affects around the external auditory meatus and the skin behind and below the ear. Atopic eczema affects the whole ear. Kerato-acanthoma appear as rapidly growing lesions on the helix.

Chilblains of the ear are common, painful and itchy.

126:True 127:False 128:True 129:True 130:True
A rare complication but if pulmonary fibrosis occurs it is worth looking at drug therapy as a cause.

131:True 132:True 133:False 134:True 135:False
Flat feet are common especially in children, usually they are asymptomatic. Although more than 50% of 2 year olds have the condition by the time they reach 10 years it occurs in less than 10%. Surgery is a last resort, physiotherapy and orthotic devices are the treatment of choice.

136:True 137:False 138:False 139:False 140:False
The expenses of running a practice are divided into three main groups. Those directly reimbursed by the FHSA Those partly reimbursed by the FHSA, e.g. staff salaries. Those which are included in the expenses element of the GP reimbursement and increased annually in line with the Review Body recommendations.

141:True 142:False 143:True 144:True 145:False.
These two conditions have a lot of similarities, sharing the same histology and the same age sex distribution. They occur in the 60-70 age group with a male:female ratio of 1:2. They are commoner in Caucasians especially of Scandinavian origin. There are no typical plasma protein changes.

146:True 147:False 148:True 149:False
Attico-antral perforations are the dangerous ones and they produce a foul

smelling discharge. The perforation is marginal and cholesteatoma may be produced.

Even alarge central perforation may be repaired after the otorrhoea has resolved.

A marginal peforation should be referred without delay.

150:False 151:False 152 :True 153:True 154:True 155:True
Aluminium salts cause constipation, magnesium salts diarrhoea.

Cisapride does not have dopamine receptor antagonist properties and therefore does not cause the dystonic reactions of metoclopramide.

Intermenstrual bleeding with misoprostol occurs because it is a prostaglandin analogue, it can result in menorrhagia, intermenstrual bleeding and postmenopausal bleeding.

The raised prolactin induced by metoclopramide can lead to galactorrhoea and gynaecomastia.

The confusion induced by H_2 receptor antagonists is reversible on stopping the drug, it can also occur in a younger age group.

Omeprazole is also associated with severe skin reactions in the absence of photophobia.

156:True 157:True 158:False 159:True 160:False
Avascular necrosis is a consequence of the interruption of the blood supply to the femoral head. Precipitating factors include a fall on the hip even without a fracture, dislocation of the hip, vasculitis, SLE, and being on NSAIDs. Deep sea divers are particularly at risk because of nitrogen bubbles causing emboli or compression of vascular channels.

Onset may be insidious but often there is a dramatic onset of pain. X-ray changes take time to develop, bone scans show early changes.

161:False 162:True 163:True 164:False 165:True
Amiodarone does not impair left ventricular function to any significant extent and can be used safely in failure. The majority of patients develop

corneal deposits but they do not interfere with vision. Thyroid function tests may show a hypo or a hyperthyroid picture but clinical symptoms rarely develop.

Photosensitivity is very common but does respond to total skinblock creams.

166:True 167:False 168:False 169:False 170:True
Air travel is being undertaken by an increasing proportion of the population. Dehydration occurs which thickens secretions and therefore vital capacity can be reduced still further.

Epileptics are vulnerable to a mixture of hypoxia, fatigue and stress which will all increase fit frequency.

Diabetics on oral agents should take their drugs as per local times. Diabetics on insulin do need to change their dosage regimes and this depends whether the flight is eastbound or westbound.

Motion sickness on aircraft decreases with age and with flying experience.

Gas trapped in the eye or any internal cavity will expand on increasing altitude therefore patients should not fly until all the gas is absorbed, possibly 6-12 weeks.

171:False 172:False 173:False 174:True 175:False
Fundholders have their prescribing costs included in their general fund. Savings on the indicative budgets cannot be carried forward. Formularies are not compulsory they are to be 'encouraged'.

If drug spending is found to be excessive without clinical justification the GP can be called before a hearing in front of 3 doctors and a withholding of remuneration can result from this.

If the FHSA is aware of patients whose drug therapy is expensive this can be allowed for in the calculation of the budget.

176:False 177:True 178:True 179:False 180:True
Nocturnal diarrhoea is rare in irritable bowel syndrome. One painless variety of the syndrome is profuse diarrhoea on waking in the morning. Pain is often related to menstrual disorder and the patient may have a lot of

gynaecological investigations prior to recognition of the problem. If painful the pain is typically relieved by defaecation.

181:True 182:True 183:False 184:False 185:False
Antenatal care is done in a blind routine fashion by some health care workers. Concepts of care have been handed down from hospital obstetric practice in an unquestioning manner. In one survey only 44% of small for gestational age babies were detected antenatally. Also for every one born with a correct diagnosis 2.5 were given the diagnosis incorrectly.

186:False 187:False 188:False 189:False 190:True
Breast lumps occurring under 30 years of age are usually fibroadenomata. Over 30 years it is either a cyst or a carcinoma. Aspiration is an easy technique for a GP, if the lesion is solid or the aspirate blood stained, referral is indicated. There is a 30% chance of a cyst recurring or further cysts developing.

Cyclical mastalgia rarely requires treatment, oil of evening primrose oil is effective, but is expensive.

191:True 192:True 193:False 194:False 195:True
Diabetics of any age are exempt. Pregnant women and the elderly are not exempt. First degree relatives of those with glaucoma can get a free test.

People on income support but not those receiving a rent rebate can also get a free test.

196:True 197:True 198:True 199:False 200:True
Charges can be made for ear piercing because it is a treatment not usually provided by a general practitioner.

Housing letter payments are often dealt with on a local basis. Payment is often made by the local council or housing association.

201:False 202:False 203:True 204:True 205:False
Rheumatic fever does not present with atrial fibrillation but rheumatic heart disease does. Thyrotoxicosis and alcoholic causes are relatively common, even American presidents are not exempt.

206:True 207:False 208:False 209:False 210:False
Normal pressure hydrocephalus is a reversible cause of the symptoms of dementia. The usual progression of the triad of symptoms is of gait disturbance of which apraxia (forgetting how to walk) is the commonest. Following this cognitive impairment occurs and then urinary incontinence develops. The symptoms are temporarily reversed by lumbar puncture. Approximately 50% of patients are improved by shunts, but the operative procedure has a high incidence of complications.

211:False 212:False 213:False 214:False 215:False
Following admission for an act of deliberate self harm 20% of patients will require admission to a psychiatric unit. 25% of all patients will repeat the episode at least once in the next year. No amount of psychiatric or social help seems to reduce the incidence. 'Help' lines are useful in individual cases but have not reduced the overall incidence, About 2% will successfully commit suicide within the next year.

216:True 217:True 218:False 219:True 220:False
Polycythemia vera may well present with a vascular incident secondary to haemodynamic changes. Increased turnover of cells leads to hyperuricaemia and gout may be a presentation. Itching is a common presentation.

Approximately 30% terminate as acute leukaemia and the incidence of this is increased by radiotherapy or chlorambucil therapy.

221:True 222:True 223:False 224:False 225:False
Sudden loss of vision in a migrainous episode is associated with complete recovery. Central retinal vein occlusion can lead to an extensive haemorrhage visible at the fundus. The visual loss typically develops over a period of a few hours.

Senile macular degeneration produces a gradually progressive loss of central vision with preservation of peripheral vision.

Optic neuritis presents with gradual loss in the 20-45 age group with intact peripheral vision.

Toxic optic neuropathy may be due to heavy cigarette smoking or alcohol intake, again peripheral vision remains intact.

226:True 227:False 228:False 229:False 230:False
The inclusion of child surveillance as a part of general practice was one of the more positive aspects of the 1990 contract. A GP must either undergo further training or have had special experience in order to be included on the list of approved doctors. The child must register separately for inclusion on the child surveillance list. Child clinics are not eligible for a payment as a health promotion clinic and immunisations are subject to target payment regulations. Any suitably trained doctor within the practice can perform the check and some of the tests still remain more the responsibility of the health visitors.

231:True 232:True 233:False 234:False 235:True
SLE is the commonest autoimmune disease in child bearing women. The rate of miscarriage is 70%, some people who miscarry repeatedly, develop SLE in later life.

High follicular levels of LH correlate with failure to conceive and recurrent miscarriage.

An abnormal parental karyotype is present in 5% of those couples who have recurrent miscarriages.

236:True 237:True 238:False 239:True 240:False
Neonates and older children are little affected by RSV. Stridor is indicative of croup not bronchiolitis. In the UK it has a strict seasonal pattern occurring between December and May. Examination of the throat is a problem in acute epiglottides which is caused by *Haemophilus influenza* infection.

241:True 242:True 243:True 244:True 245:True
Head injury is often followed by a variety of symptoms, hypochondriasis, fatigue and irritability are the most common. They can occur even when there is no definite evidence of brain damage. Depressive and schizophrenic-like psychoses are more common. The reason why suicide is more common is not known. Personality disorders are more common especially after frontal lobe damage.

246:True 247:False 248:True 249:False 250:True
Topical steroid absorption is enhanced by urea and by occlusion. This includes nappies and plastic pants. It takes about 4 g of steroid for a single

application to the trunk, 1 g to the arm, 2 g to the leg, 1 g to the hand and foot.

Local side effects of prolonged steroid use are thinning of the skin, acne, mild depigmentation and increased hair growth. Ointments are indicated for dry conditions and creams for moist conditions.

251:True 252:False 253:False 254:True 255:True
Ischaemic ulcers are typically painful presenting for the first time in those over 70 years of age. They are punched out, necrotic and found anywhere on the lower leg or foot. Venous ulcers tend to be painless, pigmented with marked induration and oedema. The surrounding skin may be eczematous.

256:False 257:True 258:False 259:True 260:True
The average age of menarche in the UK is 13 years of age. The periods stop at an average age of 50 years. There are a lot of 'old wives tales' about periods, it is often quoted but untrue that an early menarche begets a late menopause. Estimation of LH and FSH is the most reliable method of determining that symptoms are due to the menopause.

261:True 262:False 263:True 264:False 265:True
Epiphora often occurs because the irritant effect of having dry eyes causes an overflow of tears. It is associated with sarcoid and also autoimmune diseases such as rheumatoid arthritis. Schirmer's test is diagnostic. Sjörgren's syndrome is an autoimmune disease in which dry eyes are but one feature.

People with entropion often have epiphora.

266:False 267:True 268:True 269:True 270:True
Most malignant lesions have reached 1 cm in diameter before they are recognised. In the absence of other symptoms it is probably benign. If less than this size benign lesions are round or oval in shape, malignant ones have a scalloped or notched border. Malignant lesions can vary in colour from black to light brown. They may have a reddish tint due to inflammation. Benign lesions never have any evidence of erythema either within or around them. Crusting oozing or bleeding all indicate a need for referral.

271:False 272:False 273:False 274:True 275:False
The main indication of lithium treatment is to prevent the relapses in bipolar affective disorders. It is only available as an oral preparation and is of no value in acute episodes of illness.

It does not cause a chronic nephropathy and changes in urea and electrolytes are reversible on stopping the drug. Thyroid enlargement may occur and thyroid function tests should be monitored regularly.

276:True 277:True 278:False 279:True 280:True
The consent must also state whether the patient wishes to view the report. The patient has the right to provide a statement of his/her views to be attached to the report in the event of disagreement with the doctor over the content.

The doctor should keep a copy for 6 months only and the patient has a right to view this. If the patient requests a copy the doctor can charge a reasonable fee for providing one.

If there is a problem about divulging a patient's records it may well be prudent to consult your medical defence organisation.

281:True 282:True 283:False 284:False 285:True
Schizoid personalities are emotionally cold, introspective and self sufficient to a fault. They are aloof and ill at ease in company, they lack warmth and it is difficult to discover their real problems.

Self dramatisation is a feature of hysterical personalities.

286:True 287:True 288:True 289:True 290:True
Measuring the middle is not a simple matter and it is important to be clear about the difference between the mode, mean and median.

291:True 292:True 293:True 294:True 295:True
The first three questions are the cardinal rules for the treatment of undescended testes. The only other point is that some people think that 2 years is the latest age by which a testes should be placed in the scrotum because this increases fertility even more. A hernial sac is present at most operations, but usually it is asymptomatic.

296:True 297:True 298:False 299:True 300:True
In differentiating between depression and dementia, the symptoms develop more rapidly in the former. Complaints of memory loss would suggest that insight is retained, depressive symptoms are worse in the morning. Rather than 'don't know' demented patients tend to reply with near miss or inappropriate replies.

301:False 302:True 303:False 304:False
Long term follow up in hospital does not favour outcome and is probably an inappropriate use of resources. Psychological support is best effected by the primary health care team. Tamoxifen if given for 5 years has been shown to improve survival and decrease the risk of recurrence. Cancer in the opposite breast is 6 fold greater in those already having a malignancy, it is especially greatest for those who develop their first tumour under 40 years of age.

Hormone manipulation is often used first because of the decreased incidence of side effects. However the response rate is only 30% compared to 60% for chemotherapy.

305:True 306:True 307:True
Although all the women were upset by the experience, just over 50% had lasting effects, usually involving negative feelings about themselves, about men and about sex. Their ability to form lasting relationships was severely hampered.

308:True 309:True 310:False 311:False 312:False
Only after employment for one month is a new employee eligible for a minimum period of notice based on the length of service. A written reason for dismissal must be given on request only after 2 years of service. Absence due to maternity is only payable after 26 weeks of employment but paid time off must be given for antenatal care.

313:False 314:False 315:True 316:True
Sumatriptan is a 5HT analogue which probably causes cranial blood vessels to constrict. It is administered via an sc injection or orally. About 40% of patients will get a recurrence of headache and of those 70% will obtain relief from a further dose. It is contra-indicated in hemiplegic migraine, in those with unstable angina and uncontrolled hypertension. There has been an increasing incidence in the reports of ventricular arrhythmias occurring with the drug. It should not be given less than 12 hours after ergotamine and these

preparations should not be given within 12 hours of sumatriptan administration.

317:False 318:False 319:True 320:True 321:False
The average practitioner will have 2-3 new patients with gout per year, 20% of patients will have a family history. It is 6 times commoner in males than females. Chronic tophaecous gout is now rare, but that and renal gout with calculi are indications for allopurinol treatment. 25-40% of those with gout will have or will develop hypertension. Triglyceride levels are higher in gout sufferers.

322:True 323:True 324:True 325:True 326:True
Systemic gold therapy for rheumatoid arthritis may produce oral pigmentation similar to that of Addison's disease. Bulimia leads to parotid enlargement and erosion of the teeth due to regurgitation of acid. Erythema multiforme may cause extensive crusting of the lips or intra oral vesicles and bullae.

Intra oral bullae are a prominent feature of pemphigus vulgaris, they are either yellow or haemorrhagic and burst to leave an area of ulceration. Lichen planus classically affects the mouth giving erosive lesions or producing 'cotton wool' patches.

327:False 328:True 329:True 330:True 331:True
Only residents of nursing homes, residential homes and other long stay institutions are recommended to have the vaccine. In non pandemic years health care workers are not included. Patients vulnerable to acute infections because of a variety of chronic diseases should also be immunised.

332:False 333:True 334:False 335:False 336:False
Maternity medical fees are payable to all doctors, however those on the obstetric list receive a higher fee. The fees are payable for all pregnancies once the patient has signed the FP 24, if she subsequently decides that she wants a termination then a fee is payable. The GP does not need to attend the confinement. Post natal visit fees are only payable for visits up to the 14th day.

337:False 338:False 339:True 340:True 341:False
About 90% of patients will stop bleeding spontaneously. However the mortality rate is still about 10% and is not reduced by urgent endoscopy.

Drugs, such as ranitidine do not stop bleeding but some studies show that they prevent rebleeding. Gastric ulcers are more likely to rebleed than duodenal, also if blood vessels are visible at endoscopy a rebleed is more likely.

342:True 343:True 344:True 345:False 346:False
Terfenadine is an OTC antihistamine and there have been reports of serious cardiac arrhythmias if given with erythromycin or systemic anti fungal agents. Ciprofloxacin causes a potentiation of theophyline levels. Theophyline has a narrow therapeutic window and therefore toxic effects can occur. Cimetidine potentiates the effect of oral anticoagulants including warfarin. There is no significant interaction between allopurinol and captopril, it is included in the manufacturers list of interactions because of the risk of renal damage in patients with gout.

347:True 348:False 349:True 350:False 351:True 352:False
Follow up studies of opiate users show that after 7 years 25-33% are abstinent but 10-20% have died from drug related causes. Methadone liquid is used as an aid to withdrawal because it cannot be used intravenously, unlike the tablets which can be crushed and injected.

Cocaine and hallucinogens are 'recreational' drugs associated with the more privileged groups in society. Chronic amphetamine abuse is associated with a paranoid psychosis indistinguishable from paranoid schizophrenia.

353:True 354:False 355:True 356:False
Angular cheilitis is characterised by painful fissures at the angles of the mouth, *Candida* often combines with *Staph. aureus* to produce the infection. Denture stomatitis is usually found under a complete upper denture and the fitting surface is an important reservoir of the organism. A ranula is a mucus retention cyst and is caused by obstruction of the duct of a minor salivary gland. Sjörgren's syndrome is a triad of dry mouth, dry eyes and a connective tissue disorder.

357:True 358:False 359:False 360:True
Symptoms most correlating with peptic ulcer disease are, epigastric pain with a definite food association, night pain, periodicity of symptoms and prompt predictable antacid relief. A positive family history is also important.

PAPER 3

1:True 2:True 3:True 4:False 5:True
Dopamine inhibits prolactin, therefore dopamine agonists such as bromocriptine inhibit prolactin release and are used to treat prolactinomas. Conversely dopamine blockers such as metoclopramide will stimulate prolactin release.

6:True 7:True 8:True 9:False 10:False
Ototoxicity induced by quinine is usually reversible on stopping the drug but if it is given in the first trimester of pregnancy it may cause hearing loss in the baby. The hearing loss induced by frusemide occurs if the drug is given rapidly intravenously, it is typically transient. However the loss may be permanent if aminoglycosides are given concurrently.

Erythromycin is only ototoxic if given in high doses.

11:True 12:True 13:False 14:False 15:True
Postmenopausal bleeding is defined as any vaginal bleeding occurring 6 months after the last period. It should always be investigated. Exogenous oestrogens from whatever source can cause bleeding. Polyps can still occur in this age group and urethral caruncles do bleed. If the discharge is profuse and offensive, cervical cancer is a distinct possibility, but senile vaginitis also leads to vaginal infection.

16:False 17:False 18:True 19:False 20:True
Coronary artery bypass is highly successful with an operative mortality of less than 3% in the UK. Patients with improved lifespan after operation are those with triple vessel disease, unstable angina and blockage of the left main coronary artery. The results of grafting are better if an artery rather than a vein is used.

Operative mortality is greater in females and those with unstable angina. The recurrence of angina occurs at a steady rate of about 3-4% per annum.

21:True 22:False 23:False 24:False 25:True
Hysteria is a difficult and dangerous diagnosis to make, it is easy to miss genuine physical and psychiatric morbidity. Depression and anxiety are extremely common and a trial of drug therapy is often worthwhile. Hysteria

is a diagnosis of younger life and should not be made in those over 40 years of age.

Belle indifference and amnesia are very rare.

26:True 27:True 28:False 29:True 30:True
By February 1991, 89% of all 2 year old children had received MMR vaccine. The vaccine is not contraindicated in those who are HIV positive but it is in those who are immunocompromised such as on chemotherapy for leukaemia.

The rates of laboratory confirmed rubella in pregnancy have fallen from 164 in 1987 to 20 in 1990. Although meningoencephalitis has been reported following exposure to the vaccine it is much less than the rate for mumps prior to introduction of the vaccine.

31:False 32:True 33:True 34:True 35:True
30% of women and 33% of men smoke. However in the 11-15 age group 7% of boys and 9% of girls smoke and this is a decreasing incidence in both groups. Male smokers consume an average of 20 cigarettes daily and females 15 daily.

Gastrointestinal and psychiatric problems plus accidents account for the increased consultation rate of those with alcohol problems. Heavy drinkers have an increased incidence of cancer of the oral cavity, larynx and oesophagus. There was an increased rate of breast cancer in one survey.

36:True 37:False 38:False 39:True 40:False
Post viral fatigue syndrome is a complex subject. The overwhelming feature is fatigue and fatiguability that is both physical and mental. Approximately 75% of the patients have a significant psychiatric problem and over 50% have depression of such severity that a trial of antidepressants is worthwhile. Prolonged rest is not advised, patients need to regain control of their illness and need to be encouraged to increase activity.

41:False 42:True 43:True 44:False 45:True
Episcleritis causes slight or no pain with normal vision and usually settles without treatment. Conjunctival haemorrhage should be painless with normal vision. Keratitis causes impairment of vision if the ulcer or opacity is near the visual axis. Acute glaucoma causes severe pain with vomiting and

severe visual impairment. Finally iritis could also cause an increase in floaters and the pupil would be small and distorted.

46:True 47:True 48:True 49:False 50:False
Infected eczema is usually an endogenous eczema with a secondary staphylococcal infection. With scabies look for burrows along the sides of the fingers. Pustular psoriasis will probably also occur on the soles of the feet as well. Ichthyosis causes a scaly dry skin and erythema multiforme has a characteristic rash of a large vesicle with a surrounding red halo.

51:True 52:False 53:False 54:True 55:True
If the dehydration is significant the eyes are sunken and crying produces few tears, the skin is doughy and there is tachycardia and tachypnoea. The mouth is dry and the fontanelle if open, is sunken. Weight loss is not reliable, a child with diarrhoea who has been starved but is well hydrated may have lost a visible amount of weight.

56:False 57:True 58:True 59:False 60:True
Acute asthma is often underdiagnosed and underestimated by both patient and the doctor, and undue reliance placed on bronchodilators. Peak flow levels at this age should be a good predictor of severity whereas the extent of expiratory wheeze is not related. Tachycardia greater than 120 and pulsus paradoxus are good indicators of a severe attack.

Young men in their late teenage and early twenties are vulnerable to the development of spontaneous pneumothorax.

61:True 62:True 63:True 64:True 65:True
In addition to the conditions listed obesity can also lead to a worsening of arthritis and an increase in ischaemic heart disease and stroke. However do remember that it can be secondary to drug therapy, e.g. steroids, pizotifen, and to various medical conditions.

66:True 67:True 68:True 69:False 70:True
When intra ocular pressure rises there is transient oedema of the cornea and this can give rise to haloes. An associated red eye may mean that there is acute glaucoma or inflammation of the iris or ciliary body. Amblyopia is usually long standing often due to untreated or badly treated squint it does not give rise to headache. A pale optic disc may be due to a compressive lesion.

71:False 72:False 73:False 74:False 75:True
Some heavy drinkers are not physically dependent but conversely some moderate drinkers develop severe symptoms of withdrawal. Seizures typically occur within 10-60 hours of the last drink. The mortality of delirium tremens is about 10%. Many psychiatric symptoms including confusion, disorientation, paranoia, auditory or visual hallucinations may occur 72 hours or more after the last drink. The typical early withdrawal symptoms are tremor, sweating, anorexia, nausea, insomnia and anxiety.

76:False 77:True 78:False 79:True 80:True
SIDS shows no association with the mode or type of delivery. The risk increases with the parity especially if the pregnancies are closer together. If the mother is addicted to narcotic agents there is a 30 fold increase in risk. Twins are at risk and if one twin suffers a sudden infant death or a 'near miss' the other twin should be monitored very closely.

Children are best placed on their side or supine at night.

81:False 82:True 83:False 84:True 85:False
Hot baths cause vasodilatation enhancing penetration of the drug and increasing the risk of CNS toxicity. This toxicity is why the drug is contraindicated in pregnant women. A single application is usually sufficient to eradicate the mite and it decreases the chances of toxicity. Scabies typically does not affect the face, except in one variety that occurs in mentally handicapped patients and known as Norwegian scabies.

Itching may take 4 weeks to resolve after successful eradication of all the mites.

86:False 87:True 88:False 89:False 90:True
Hodgkin's disease typically presents with lymphadenopathy and in over half this is a cervical gland enlargement. Hepatomegaly is an indication of advanced disease and has a poor prognostic significance. Early localised disease has been treated successfully with radiotherapy whereas generalised disease is treated with chemotherapy. 'Cure' rates of between 70-80% are usual.

91:True 92:False 93:True 94:False 95:False
Agoraphobia is a disease which typically affects women. Although they are often highly dependent on their husbands there is no increase in the rate of divorce or separation.

Thoughts tend to focus on a fear of losing control e.g. fainting. Depersonalisation (feeling that ones body is unreal or remote) is a very typical symptom but this can also occur in depression. Programmed behaviour therapy is the psychological treatment that produces the best results.

96:True 97:False 98:True 99:False 100:True
The commonest drugs to cause fixed drug eruptions are NSAIDs, sulphonamides, tetracyclines and quinine. They may take up to 2 hours to develop, a brown discolouration of the skin may last for several months. The acute reaction of an oval inflammatory patch may or may not contain blisters.

101:False 102:False 103:True 104:True 105:False
Improvement grants are usually available to help GPs to improve existing premises and can be one third of the cost of approved work. Separate rooms for a trainee are desirable but not compulsory. The cost rent scheme is highly advantageous but does strictly limit the number of rooms and the maximum sizes possible. It is possible to change from cost rent to notional rent schemes but only after a district valuer assessment which can only be done every three years.

106:True 107:False 108:True 109:True 110:False
The mortality of paracetamol overdosage is not falling, the reason being due to late presentation and that the antidote treatment with acetylcysteine is ineffective if given over 15 hours after the ingestion of the drug. Although chronic alcohol ingestion worsens the outlook, acute alcohol ingestion appears to be protective. Carbamazepine, phenytoin, and phenobarbitone if taken as well worsen the prognosis.

111:False 112:False 113:True 114:True 115:True
Following on from the provisions of the Data Protection Act this provides access to hand written notes. It applies to all 'employed by the health service body'. Only notes made after November 1991 are included. As in the Data Protection Act the GP has 21 days to comply with request for access and can make a charge to the patient and can also charge for any copies provided.

116:True 117:False 118:True 119:False 120:True

Aortic stenosis is now the commonest valvular lesion in all adults, usually due to degenerative-calcific disease. A soft murmur does not exclude severe aortic stenosis especially if the patient has low output cardiac failure. In contrast mitral stenosis is invariably due to rheumatic heart disease. Mitral regurgitation is most commonly due to the same factors as aortic stenosis. A prolapsing mitral valve is the next most common cause.

70% of patients over 70 will have a murmur.

121:True 122:True 123:True 124:False 125:False

Risk factors for osteoporosis can be divided into high, medium and low. Alcoholism is a medium risk factor and cigarette smoking although a risk factor carries a lower risk. The others quoted are high risk factors.

126:False 127:True 128:True 129:True 130:True

Fragile X is so called because there is a gap in the long arm of the X chromosome which can be seen on examination of the amniotic fluid antenatally. Carrier females are usually of normal intelligence but 10% have mild mental retardation. It is the commonest form of X linked mental retardation and the children typically have bat ears a large jaw and maxillary hypoplasia.

131:True 132:False 133:True 134:False 135:True

Doctors must be available for 26 hours per week spread over 5 days with a possibility of 4 days if the doctor is undertaking health related activity elsewhere within the public service. They have to be available for 42 weeks per year. Times and places of availability must be approved. An allowance for travelling is included in the 26 hours of availability.

Job sharing GPs must have a combined availability of 5 days but each doctor is not expected to be available on each of these days.

136:True 137:False 138:True 139:False 140:False

Drugs which undergo significant first pass metabolism by the liver must be given with caution to those patients with liver disease, for instance coma may be precipitated in the cirrhotic by the use of analgesics containing opiates.

Acyclovir along with many antibiotics is excreted unchanged by the kidney.

141:False 142:True 143:True 144:False 145:False
Before ovulation the cervix is closed and firm. During ovulation it is fully open admitting a finger tip and is wet due to the production of stringy mucus. Within 48 hours of ovulation the cervix closes and becomes firm again, the mucus becomes rubbery and thick forming a plug.

Tests which predict ovulation measure LH secretion. Basal temperature rises during ovulation and stays raised in the luteal phase.

146:False 147:False 148:True 149:False 150:False
Parkinson's disease has an incidence of 1:1000 in middle life rising to 1:200 in the elderly.

In the latter it typically presents with rigidity. Levodopa is effective in reducing symptoms but its effect lasts between 5-8 years. Selegiline is effective both early and late after levodopa has failed to be effective and may delay progression of the disease.

Dementia is a common feature of late disease.

151:True 152:True 153:True 154:True 155:True
Fibroids are often asymptomatic, surgery is usually indicated if the bleeding is heavy or the fibroid is above 14-16 weeks in size. GnRH analogues are not licensed for use but certain centres are now using them to shrink fibroids prior to the menopause or surgery.

HRT causes fibroids to increase in size if not monitored closely.

156:False 157:True 158:True 159:True 160:True
Anxiety may be triggered by a multitude of factors including physical illness, caffeine ingestion, alcohol withdrawal or the use of drugs such as sympathomimetics or antihistamines.

Treatment is directed to both the somatic and psychological aspects. MAOIs are very effective in anxiety especially when there is a phobic element.

161:True 162:True 163:False 164:True 165:False
Congenital abnormalities occur in 7% of babies born to epileptic mothers. Sodium valproate increases the risk of spina bifida to 1-2% (normally 0.023%

of all births). The incidence of congenital heart disease in the babies of mothers taking phenytoin is 8%, it is also associated with orofacial cleft deformities.

Carbamazepine appears to be relatively safe, it is chloramphenicol which causes bone marrow suppression. Warfarin is associated with CNS defects, heparin is not implicated.

166:False 167:True 168:True 169:False 170:False
The peak incidence of acute suppurative otitis media is between 4-8 years of age. The majority of infections are mild and only 10% of these are bacterial.

About 90% of severe cases are bacterial. Only 1% develop chronic suppurative otitis media and of these only a few will get mastoiditis.

171:False 172:False 173:True 174:True 175:True
Pulmonary embolism is the commonest cause of death in the UK associated with pregnancy. Two thirds occur post natally. Increasing age and increasing parity are risk factors. Complicated delivery also increases the risk. Women who have had thromboembolism in the past have a 1:10 to 1:20 risk of a further episode and anticoagulation throughout the pregnancy with heparin is usually advised.

176:True 177:True 178:True 179:True 180:False
Appendicitis is still missed, especially in the young and the old. The incidence in a population is inversely proportional to the amount of dietary fibre consumed by that population. Therefore the incidence in the UK is decreasing. Retrocaecal appendices are associated with atypical symptoms and a high retrocaecal appendicitis may mimic the symptoms of renal tract infection.

181:False 182:False 183:False 184:True 185:True
The American criteria for consent are much stricter than the British. In Britain the doctor need only give the patient enough information to make a rational choice rather than provide details of every rare complication. Under the Gillick judgement, patients under 16 years of age can give consent if they are thought mature enough to understand the implications. Oral consent is as valid as written consent, the problem is proving that it was given. Under the Police and Criminal Evidence Act, intimate samples need the

consent of patients over 17, of the patient and parent between 14-17, and of parent alone under 14 years of age.

186:False 187:False 188:True 189:True 190:True
The inclusion of certain items and the exclusion of others from the minor surgical list fails to make a lot of sense to doctors who have been doing surgical procedures for a long time before the 'new contract'.

Intra-articular, periarticular and injections of varicose veins are included in the minor surgery list. Curettage, cautery or cryocautery to warts and verrucae and other skin lesions are also allowed.

191:False 192:False 193:True 194:True 195:True
Acute lymphoblastic leukaemia is the commonest 85% with 14% acute myeloblastic. The average age of onset of the former is 3-5 years of age and of the latter neonates. The best prognosis is for ALL in boys aged 1-8 years. The overall survival of the disease after completion of five years treatment is 65%.

Maintenance cytotoxics are usually continued for 3 years once remission has been achieved.

196:False 197:False 198:False 199:False 200:True
There are relatively few absolute contraindications to HRT. The main one quoted is oestrogen dependent tumours, however recent evidence has cast some doubt on this. Diabetes is only a relative contraindication.

All routes of treatment are helpful with the symptoms of atrophic vaginitis. Lipid levels are favourably affected by unopposed oestrogen, it is the progestogenic component which appears to cause problems with elevation of lipid levels. If given for 10 years it has been estimated that the incidence of osteoporotic fractures would be halved.

201:False 202:True 203:False 204:False 205:False
Impotence due to an organic cause is usually of insidious onset. It is commoner in patients with vascular diseases and various neurological abnormalities e.g. diabetic neuropathy, multiple sclerosis.

Papaverine is given by intracavernosal injection and an erection should last 3 hours maximum. It is usually limited to twice weekly use. Vacuum condoms are not available on NHS prescriptions.

206:False 207:True 208:True 209:False 210:True
This condition of extreme self neglect usually affects people who live alone. The incidence is 0.5 per 1000 population so most GPs will have one patient on their list. 50% have a normal mental state but the rest have significant psychopathology. Physical illness is very common and often severe leading to a mortality of 50%. Admission to hospital worsens the condition with apathy developing. Patients tend to be of above average intelligence.

211:True 212:False 213:False 214:False 215:True
This is a common condition usually occurring in young children under 3 years of age. The mechanism of injury is typically that of a traction injury to the childs arm when it is held in an extended position. Such as being pulled onto the feet by the hands or being 'bounced' with the arms above the head. It is commoner on the left side. The annular ligament probably slips or has a small tear which allows subluxation of the radial head. X-ray shows no abnormality. Reduction is simply done by forced supination, anaesthesia not being necessary.

216:False 217:True 218:False 219:True 220:True
Crohn's disease is characterised by pain and diarrhoea but rarely blood. Rectal involvement is rare in Crohn's disease unlike ulcerative colitis where 95% will have rectal involvement. Annular strictures are common in Crohn's but in ulcerative colitis they are an indication that malignant change may have occurred.

221:False 222:False 223:False 224:False 225:False
Over 75 screening was one of the less popular parts of the government reforms. It does not attract an item of service payment and is included in the terms of service. It has to be carried out annually, 90% of over 75 year olds will see their GP at some other time during that year and the 5% who do not will be well. The cost benefits of screening are highly contentious and have not yet been shown. Most surveys show that very little illness and few social problems are uncovered.

226:True 227:False 228:False 229:True 230:False
If retinoblastoma is a cause of squint, instead of a red reflex there is the typical white reflex. The majority of squints in children are non-paralytic. If treatment is left until 8 years the eye will be amblyopic and surgery will only be cosmetic. If patching of the good eye is excessive cases have been reported of it becoming amblyopic. To maximise sight, referral should be made before 6 months of age.

231:False 232:True 233:True 234:True 235:False
Cervical erosion is twice as common in pill users than in a matched population who have not taken the pill. Benign breast diseases are suppressed in long term users of combined oral contraceptives.

Endometrial cancer and ovarian cancer rates appear to be reduced by about 50% in those who have had two years or more of continual ovulation suppression with oral contraceptives. Cervical cancer rates are not reduced, some data would suggest an increased incidence but cervical cancer is so related to sexual activity, it is difficult to work out a relationship.

236:True 237:True 238:False 239:False 240:False
Addison's disease may present insidiously with episodic vomiting and diarrhoea accompanied by weight loss. Abdominal pain is often severe and colicky. Eventually symptoms may lead to an Addisonian crisis with a shocked, hypotensive patient.

Chronic insufficiency is marked by postural hypotension. The typical blood picture is hyponatraemia, hyperkalaemia and a raised blood urea.

241:False 242:False 243:False 244:True 245:False
Dementia is not preventable by social support but depression is reduced. A well balanced diet helps general health and may reduce cardiovascular disease but does not reduce dementia. Eating beef has not as yet been shown to cause a transmittable form of dementia. Treatment of hypertension over the years decreases atherosclerosis and therefore the incidence of multi-infarct dementia. Over 75 screening by GPs has not yet been shown to decrease dementia or related problems.

246:True 247:True 248:False 249:False 250:False
Restless legs syndrome has been described for over 100 years. It has been associated with many factors most of them disproved, however, it may be the presenting complaint in uraemia.

It typically is worse in the evening and at night causing insomnia. Benzodiazepines are said to help. There is no association with coffee or tea ingestion.

251:False 252:False 253:False 254:False 255:False
Audit is now a contractual obligation on behalf of general practitioners.

There are lots of ways and viewpoints to how it should be practised. Audit is a process of education through experience, not looking for mistakes. It must be free from blame or guilt if it is to be successful. It should be dynamic with the aim of helping people to do their jobs better. It can illuminate problem areas but it is not solely concerned with problem solving. The boundaries between audit and research are often blurred.

256:True 257:True 258:True 259:True 260:True
All are available from pharmacists without an NHS prescription and all cost less than the current price of such a prescription.

261:False 262:True 263:True 264:True 265:False
Pyelonephritis is the commonest medical emergency in pregnancy occurring in 1% of pregnancies. It typically presents in the second and third trimesters and in about one quarter of cases reoccurs throughout the rest of the pregnancy. There is an increased association with pre-term labour, fetal growth retardation and perinatal death. 4-quinolone antibiotics are contraindicated in pregnancy because experimental work has shown an association with arthropathy in the fetus.

266:True 267:True 268:True 269:True 270:True
Ankylosing spondylitis is usually of gradual onset with low backache and morning stiffness. 15% present with a peripheral arthritis. Iritis occurs in 25% of cases, the ESR is raised in 80%. 6% have it as a familial trait and it is associated with specific histo-compatibility antigens.

271:False 272:True 273:True 274:True 275:True
Dermatitis artefacta is the term given to self induced lesions which characteristically have straight sides. Polymorphic eruption of pregnancy occurs in 1:150 pregnancies usually primigravidae occurring in the second and third trimesters and clearing within 2-3 weeks of delivery. Nodular prurigo often occur on the hands and heal to leave white scars with follicular openings in them. Dermatitis herpetiformis typically occurs in young adults, it has an intensely itchy vesicular rash with a psoriatic distribution. Lichen simplex needs to be treated by interrupting the itch/scratch cycle, then the lichenified rash disappears.

276:True 277:True 278:True 279:True 280:True
Severe puerperal psychosis presents in the early puerperium. It may present as psychotic depression or hypomania. Those with hypomania often become depressed at the end of a spell of being 'high'. Some show a fluctuating pattern. ECT has been shown to be of benefit and often produces a rapid remission. With treatment it tends to run a course of about 2-3 months of illness, the risk of infanticide during this time is increased.

281:True 282:True 283:False 284:True 285:False
Campylobacter often starts as a febrile illness after an incubation period of 3-5 days. If bleeding is present in a shigella infection this is an indication that antibiotic treatment may be necessary. In giardia, pain is not a feature but watery diarrhoea is. Salmonella without blood stream invasion is often a relatively mild diarrhoeal episode only lasting a few days.

286:False 287:False 288:False 289:False 290:True
Streptokinase is given via an infusion and is therefore unsuitable for community use. Anistreplase is given by IV bolus. Aspirin given as a concomitant has been shown to decrease mortality further. Age alone is no reason for limitation of use of these drugs. Streptokinase cannot be repeated within the next 12 months. Anything that may bleed such as a recent surgical procedure or a recently diagnosed ulcer is a contraindication to the use of these drugs.

291:True 292:True 293:True 294:False 295:True
At 7 months 90% can stand with support and 70% can sit without support. 75% can say three words at 12 months. At 30 months the majority will be dry in the day but not at night. At 54 months 75% of girls and 60% of boys can dress themselves.

296:True 297:False 298:True 299:True 300:True
Hypertrophic obstructive cardiomyopathy is important because it is the commonest cause of sudden death in apparently healthy young adults especially athletes. It was found in half of athletes who died during participation in a sporting activity. It is an inherited condition and it occurs at any age from neonate to old age. All family members should be investigated preferably by echocardiography. The commonest presentation is with shortness of breath often accompanied by syncope and angina. The electrocardiograph typically shows changes of left ventricular hypertrophy.

301:True 302:False 303:False 304:True 305:False
Neck pain is very common, women are more prone than men in a ratio of 2:1. It is usually a benign transitory condition with 85% of patients symptom free within 1-4 weeks. About 18-20% relapse within 2 years. Soft collars are of no proven benefit and they are not prescribable on an FP10. NSAIDs have a role in reducing the severity of symptoms and in selected patients manipulation is of definite benefit.

306:False 307:True 308:False 309:False 310:True 311:False
Herpes simplex infection usually heals within 6-10 days with topical acyclovir. Recurrence rate is less than 5% if treatment is commenced promptly. Visual acuity is not affected with peripheral lesions but is more likely if the central cornea is affected. Referral is indicated because of the potential threat to vision.

312:False 313:True 314:False 315:False 316:True
In women chlamydia is usually asymptomatic and causes a cervicitis rather than a vaginitis. A negative MSSU with dysuria in a sexually active woman should lead to a search for the organism. If present in pregnancy there is a 50% transmission rate to the neonate with the risk of conjunctivitis, and pneumonitis, treatment should begin before delivery.

In men the common presentation is with non specific urethritis or epididymitis, it is not associated with prostatitis.

317:True 318:False 319:True 320:True 321:True
There are about one million new case of back pain per year and the average general practitioner sees about 50 acute backs per year. Many people do not consult, however 10-15 million working days are lost per year because of back pain. 80% recover in 3-4 weeks, however in 50% of patients there is a

recurrence within the next 5 years. About one third of patients are referred for specialist opinion but only 1:200 of the original sufferers and 1:60 of those referred undergo surgery. Several studies have shown that rest, in the early stages, reduces the overall time away from work.

322:True 323:True 324:True 325:False 326:True
Irritable bowel syndrome has been treated by increasing dietary fibre, however some patients find that excess bran makes the symptoms worse. In one study, 70% of patients improved on a bland diet free of wheat and milk. Increased fermentation in the gut is directly implicated as a trigger for the condition. Metronidazole substantially alters the aerobic/anaerobic balance within the bowel and can increase the fermentation rate. Nystatin has been shown to decrease fermentation and improve symptoms. Stress is a well known trigger factor and hypnosis and relaxation techniques decrease the symptoms and the relapse rate of IBS.

327:True 328:False 329:False 330:True 331:True
Cramps especially occurring during the night are common. However there are a large number of causes which should be excluded. Drug therapy especially diuretics and sympathomimetics, even if the latter are inhaled, are frequent causes. Peripheral vascular disease and venous obstruction do not cause cramps, but cramps may coexist. About 80% of those with cirrhosis have nocturnal cramps. Lumbar spine dysfunction especially nerve involvement at the L5/S1 level is a potent cause of nocturnal cramps.

332:True 333:False 334:True 335:False 336:False
At present less than 50% of mothers breast feed their babies successfully. Whether this government target can be met is a matter of considerable doubt. Mastitis is typically caused by staphylococcus. Breast feeding does take considerably longer than bottle feeding and this point should be emphasised to reassure mothers. Obesity is rare in breast fed infants but more common in bottle fed infants. Introduction of cows milk should not take place until one year of age. The solute load is too great for children until this age. Full cream milk and not semi-skimmed should be used.

337:False 338:False 339:False 340:False 341:True
Spacer devices decrease the incidence of oral candidiasis by preventing the deposition in the mouth. Salmeterol is a long acting beta antagonist, its action is slow in onset and therefore it should be given regularly rather than p.r.n.

The Committee on Safety of Medicines has reported that salbuterol and terbutaline have not been shown to lead to a worsening of mild asthma. In adults an inhaled dosage of steroid of 1500 micrograms daily is associated with adrenal suppression. Sodium cromoglycate is of no value in an acute attack and is only indicated for prophylaxis.

342:False 343:False 344:False 345:True
Basic practice allowance is paid to principals whether they are full time or part time, for part time doctors it is rated proportionately. It is also down rated for patient numbers less than 1200 for an individual doctor. However in partnerships the total list size is pooled.

346:True 347:True 348:True 349:True 350:True
Trials comparing active and physiological management of the third stage of labour have shown that it is reduced from an average of 15 minutes to 5 minutes and that the incidence of primary post partum haemorrhage is decreased from 18% to 6%. However one study has shown that there is an increased rate of retained placenta and all studies have shown an increase in maternal vomiting and hypertension.

351:True 352:False 353:True 354:True 355:True
Clinical trials have shown benefits to the use of antidepressants in many conditions.

356:True 357:True 358:True 359:False 360:False
Closure of the ductus arteriosus usually takes place within 48 hours of birth and is brought about by muscular contraction initially and then fibrosis. Delay is associated with maternal rubella and prematurity. Indomethacin therapy does close the duct but in some cases it reopens and surgery is necessary. If untreated, 20% of patients will have died by 30 years of age and 60% by 60 years of age. Bacterial endocarditis is especially common in patients with this condition.

PAPER 4

1:True 2:True 3:True 4:True 5:True
Prospective studies have shown an association with all the factors quoted. However the most important factor associated with increased mortality after a stoke is the level of consciousness.

6:True 7:True 8:True 9:True 10:True
Amenorrhoea or oligomenorrhea accompanied by hirsutism is almost certainly due to Stein-Leventhal syndrome. Fertility is reduced and early miscarriage is common in those who do conceive.

LH is raised and FSH is depressed but the significance of this is not fully understood. Ultrasound will detect polycystic ovaries.

11:True 12:False 13:False 14:False 15:True 16:False
Because of the availability of efficient pediculocides the overall incidence of head lice is falling. Resistance does emerge and because of this most health authorities operate a 3 year rotational policy. Malathion confers a residual protective effect against reinfection which lasts up to 6 weeks. However frequent washing of the hair or swimming in chlorinated water destroys the effect. Lotions are the treatment of choice as they are more effective. Nit combing is not medically necessary but may be needed for cosmetic reasons.

17:True 18:True 19:True 20:True 21:True
Two separate studies on weight loss in the elderly have produced similar results. Weight loss of 5% in 6 months should not be ignored, 75-80% will have some pathology to account for the loss. Malignancy accounts for 20%, depression 10%. GI tract disease 15%. The reason is usually obvious at the initial examination or with simple tests. If not immediately apparent extensive tests are not helpful. Of those without an obvious reason for the loss 80% will regain some or all of the lost weight within one year.

22:False 23:False 24:False 25:True 26:False
If the diagnosis of vitamin B12 deficiency is in doubt it is still possible to confirm the diagnosis by using the Schilling test even after replacement therapy has been established. Dietary deficiency is very uncommon except in very strict vegetarians.

Vitamin B12 is now given every 3 months by injection and this appears to be adequate. However patients may become psychologically dependent and demand it more frequently. It is cheap and excess is excreted in the urine once stores are saturated. There are no clinical problems associated with more frequent injections.

27:False 28:False 29:True 30:True 31:False
Wood's light is a source of ultraviolet light from which visible light has been excluded. It does not fluoresce eczematous skin.

32:True 33:True 34:False 35:True 36:True
Depressive delusions often centre on poverty or physical illness. Initially depression may present with symptoms of dementia but these symptoms disappear with treatment of the depression. Bereavement is less likely to provoke a depressive illness than in younger age groups. Both agitation and retardation occur in significant numbers of elderly patients.

37:False 38:False 39:False 40:False 41:False
Usually cryotherapy cannot be tolerated until 7 years of age. Basal cell carcinomas are often suitable for cryotherapy but one must be sure of the histology. The usual pattern of response is a triple response followed by tissue swelling.

Liquid nitrogen does not destroy virus effectively, therefore instruments should be disposable or be sterilized between treatments.

42:False 43:False 44:False 45:True 46:False
There are still patients who miss out on their free prescriptions and it is up to doctors to advise those so entitled.

47:True 48:False 49:True 50:True 51:True
Accidents are preventable, measures such as seat belt wearing decrease death and injury. One third of all childhood deaths in the UK are due to accidents. Given that 10% of children attend their doctor each year with an accident the scope for opportunistic education is enormous. 40,000 children attend casualty departments annually with suspected poisoning, yet only 20 die, usually age 1-5 years.

52:True 53:False 54:False 55:False 56:True
Cotton wool spots are retinal infarcts in the nerve fibre layer and are of serious prognostic significance. Once early changes of retinopathy develop they rarely respond to treatment. Retinal haemorrhages only interfere with vision if the macula is involved. Papilloedema due to hypertension is usually accompanied by other signs of hypertensive retinopathy and elevation of the optic disc. In the elderly hypertensive arterio-venous changes are the first discernable retinal change.

57:False 58:False 59:True 60:False 61:True
The majority of pacemakers are inserted for sick sinus syndrome. Activity is not restricted by the pacemaker more by the underlying condition.
Primary pacemaker failure is an uncommon cause of death. The average pacemaker lasts over 5 years with some lasting 20 years.

If there is a myocardial infarct, ST and T wave changes may not be typical.

62:True 63:False 64:True 65:True 66:False
Grief reactions show an initial stage of non reaction for a few hours or days, up to 2 weeks. Delay until 4 weeks is pathological. Hostility to somebody or something is normal, only if it is extreme does it become pathological. Some degree of social isolation may occur but if extreme and prolonged may indicate atypical grief. Most patients return to work within 2 weeks. Suicidal ideas are common, they are atypical when they are strong and well formulated.

67:False 68:False 69:False 70:True 71:True
Cystic fibrosis is the commonest lethal genetic disorder in caucasians. It varies in severity and milder cases are often detected later in life. If a child is affected there is a probability of 1:4 of subsequent children having the disorder. Survival now occurs into the third and fourth decade of life. Boys will be azoospermic but girls have reduced fertility and conception is possible. 50% of adolescents will develop a degree of glucose intolerance.

72:False 73:True 74:False 75:True 76:False
So called 'brachial neuritis' is often caused by carpel tunnel syndrome especially if the pain is at night.

If bilateral, carpal tunnel is usually worse in the dominant hand. Local injections and immobilisation are often curative. It is also associated with acromegaly, amyloid, multiple myeloma, rheumatoid arthritis and pregnancy. Thenar wasting is a late feature and is rarely seen.

77:True 78:False 79:True 80:True 81:True
10% of myeloma are detected as an incidental finding whilst the patient is being investigated for something else. The classic features are of bone pain with osteolytic lesions on X-ray, and renal involvement with eosinophilic hyaline casts and slowly progressive renal failure. Bleeding may occur due to renal failure or thrombocytopenia. Peripheral neuropathy can occur especially if amyloid is associated.

82:True 83:False 84:False 85:False 86:False
Endometriosis is common and ectopic endometrium is very common. It is found in 10% of all gynaecological operations and has been reported as present in 60% of laparoscopies done for infertility. Cyclical pain, dyspareunia and a pelvic mass with lack of uterine mobility are typical signs and symptoms.

Medical treatment produces improvement within 2 months both histologically and clinically. However it fails to produce an improvement if fertility has been affected.

87:True 88:False 89:True 90:False 91:True
Females are affected more than males and the first attack is on average at 30 years of age with a steep fall in incidence after 45 years of age. 80% of patients will remit after the first attack, with relapses occurring about twice per year. In the 20% that have the progressive form of the disease they usually present at over 40 years of age. In 25% it is relatively benign with no evidence of disability after 10 years. There are no specific tests available, MRI scanning is abnormal in many patients.

92:True 93:False 94:False 95:True 96:False
The Childrens Act 1989 came into effect in October 1991. The main feature is making the wishes of the child paramount. Emergency protection orders replace Place of Safety orders, they last for 8 days and any person can apply to a court for the order. Parental access is not precluded. Police protection provisions provide for police protection for up to 72 hours if a child would otherwise suffer harm. Parental responsibility is not transferred to the police.

Care orders place the child in the care of the local authority, whereas supervision orders place the child under the supervision of a local authority or probation officer. They cannot exist together.

97:False 98:False 99:False 100:False 101:False
Acute torticollis is a common condition occuring in the 15-30 age group. It starts acutely with a sudden pain and inability to move the head. Active and passive movements are restricted and the head is typically held in a position flexed away from the pain. It is not associated with significant arthritis and there are no neurological symptoms.

102:False 103:False 104:False 105:True
Metered dose inhalers are the most effective way of giving inhaled steroids, nebulisers are very inefficient. Dry powder inhalers are slightly less inefficient than aerosol devices but are more user friendly and are also ozone friendly. Large volume spacer devices increase the intrapulmonary deposition and they are recommended for all patients on more than 1000 micrograms daily. A regular dose of 1500 micrograms in adults has been associated with adrenal suppression. Growth inhibition in children has been reported with doses of between 200-800 micrograms daily.

106:True 107:False 108:True 109:True 110:True
Urinary tract infection is underdiagnosed in young children, approximately 3% of girls and 1% of boys will have an infection by 10 years of age. About 60% have no structural abnormality with 35% having vesico-ureteric reflux. Scarring occurs with missed or inadequately treated infection.

A high index of suspicion is needed especially under 2 years of age. It may present with non specific symptoms such as convulsions, dehydration, diarrhoea, vomiting, failure to thrive, pyrexia of unknown origin or abdominal pain.

111:True 112:False 113:False 114:True 115:True
Infective endocarditis occurs on valves that are deformed such as a bicuspid aortic valve or a prolapsed mitral valve. Only 25% of patients have an obvious source of the infection. Even if treated the mortality is of the order of 20%. Plasma viscosity is replacing ESR in most laboratories.

116:True 117:True 118:False 119:True 120:False
Penicillamine stains nails yellow and chloroquine blue-grey. White nail streaks are due to minor trauma and occur in most people. Familial leuconychia stains the whole of the nail white and is inherited as an autosomal dominant trait. Tinea causes white or yellow areas and thickening of the nail. It also slows the rate of growth. Yellow nail syndrome is due to disturbance of lymphatics, the nail becomes curved longitudinally and transversely and the rate of growth slows. It is associated with lymphoedema.

121:True 122:False 123:True 124:False 125:False
Research protocols need to be carefully written and need to adhere to a strict format. If there are excessive financial inducements to a researcher an ethical committee may withhold consent. When involving patients it is very important that a very detailed explanation is given. Retrospective studies do not usually require consent from the patient. The advantage of a structured interview is that it is standardised and they do not need specialised interviewers to conduct them.

126:False 127:False 128:True 129:False 130:False
Meningococcal vaccine is not available against group B strains. The prevalence is increasing because of recent changes in the cycle of the various strains. Despite the fact that there is decreasing sensitivity to penicillin emerging, benzylpenicillin is still the treatment of choice if the disease is suspected. Rifampicin is the treatment of choice for contacts, resistance to chloramphenicol has emerged. The increased risks for household contacts is over 1000 fold.

131:False 132:True 133:True 134:True 135:True
The majority of people with bulimia are of normal weight. Fluoxetine in particular seems to have a short term beneficial effect but not as much as psychological interventions. If they become pregnant there is an increased risk of cleft lip and palate. One third of the patients have a history of anorexia nervosa and some have the two diseases together, if this is so the overall prognosis is worse than bulimia alone. Diuretic abuse, purgative abuse and excessive exercise are all associated.

136:True 137:True 138:True 139:False 140:False
For years iron supplements have been given routinely in pregnancy. Selecting those that need them is a problem. Estimating the patients haemoglobin is not an accurate reflection of the iron stores. Serum ferritin

is an expensive investigation to employ routinely in all pregnant women but it does reflect accurately the iron stores available. Demands for iron are greatest in the third trimester and maternal iron stores will be at their lowest at this stage of the pregnancy. The fetal iron stores are laid during this trimester.

141:True 142:True 143:True 144:True 145:True
Opiate analgesics cause delay in the absorption of paracetamol due to the delay in gastric emptying. Chlorpromazine and other phenothiazines increase the toxic metabolites of opiates especially pethidine, hence there is a significant increase in symptoms such as drowsiness, lightheadedness and dry mouth. Cimetidine reduces the loss of opiates from the body as it inhibits the hepatic enzymes responsible for metabolism of the opiates. Ranitidine does not appear to have the same effects. Methadone levels have been shown to be reduced by up to 60% if given with phenytoin. Lactulose does not interact and a laxative is usually necessary with opiates.

146:True 147:False 148:True 149:False 150:False
Contraceptive fees are only payable for services to female patients. A GP cannot claim for contraceptive advice or procedures on males. A procedure or appliance does not have to be performed, the fee can be claimed for advice only. Practice nurses can perform contraceptive services on behalf of a doctor.

151:True 152:True 153:True 154:False 155:False
The average list size in England fell below 2000 in October 1988. In Scotland and Wales it is considerably lower than this level. 11% of GPs are single handed, 15% are in a partnership of two, 19% in a partnership of three, the remaining 55% are in practices with four or more doctors. Only 30% practise from health centres. Workload surveys suggest that the average GP sees 138 patients per week in the surgery.

156:True 157:False 158:False 159:False 160:False
Gilbert's syndrome is a benign familial unconjugated hyperbilrubinaemia which is suffered by 2-5% of the population. The histology of the liver is typically normal. The incidence of gall stones is no greater and the jaundice is typically worsened by fasting.

161:False 162:True 163:True 164:True 165:False
Classic symptoms of moderately severe depression are early morning waking, a diurnal mood variation feeling worse in the morning and decreased libido. Delusions of poverty occur in psychotic depression. An abnormal dexamethasone suppression test occurs in some 30% of people with moderate to severe depression.

166:True 167:False 168:False 169:True 170:True
The changes at puberty are complex but show a similar pattern. The first sign in boys is testicular growth and in girls it is breast development. The major part of weight gain is due to muscle and bone increase not fat. Girls are ahead in all aspects of development. The final height is reached 4 years after the maximum growth spurt in both sexes.

171:False 172:False 173:True 174:False 175:False
Erythema chronicum migrans is a single lesion caused by the tick borne spirochaete. It has an area of expanding erythema. Erysipelas usually presents with a high fever and an unwell patient, there are large blisters with exudate. It is due to group A beta haemolytic streptococcal infection.

Erythema nodosum is the most likely diagnosis, crops of lesions on the shins occur with individual ones lasting 7-10 days in crops over 3-6 weeks. Often it is associated with sarcoid, drugs or streptococcal infection.

Acanthosis nigricans is increased pigmentation on the body associated with an internal malignancy such as the bowel or stomach.

Kaposi's sarcoma are purple/red macules or papules usually on the trunk or back which grow quickly and become nodular or form plaques. It is classically associated with AIDS.

176:True 177:False 178:False 179:True 180:True
Immersion in water leads to hydrostatic pressure supporting the circulation in the lower body. Sudden removal from the water leads to a pooling of blood in the lower legs and a decreased venous return with the consequence of hypovolaemic shock.

At 34°-35° centigrade confusion and disorientation occur. Cardiac arrhythmias start at 33° centigrade. The patient is usually semiconscious between 30°-33° centigrade and loses consciousness below this temperature.

Rewarming should never be rapid and the last statement is a practical 'rule of thumb'.

181:False 182:True 183:False 184:False 185:False
The density of a cataract does not affect the results of surgery. Retinal detachment incidence is increased but less so after extracapsular lens extraction. Thickening of the posterior capsule is a complication of extracapsular extraction, it can be dealt with by laser capsulectomy as an out patient procedure. Modern surgical techniques mean that the patient is out of bed on the day of surgery. Intraocular implants are suitable for people with any type of visual defect.

186:False 187:True 188:True 189:False 190:False
Cough occurs in 1:8 patients on ACE inhibitors and only resolves if the drug is withdrawn usually within one week. ACE inhibitors are both teratogenic and fetotoxic, they are also toxic to neonates. They inhibit the production of aldosterone and therefore cause hyponatraemia in the absence of diuretics. Skin rashes are common and occur in about 4% of patients.

191:True 192:False 193:True 194:True 195:False
Chondromalacia produces pain especially if the patella is pressed distally and the quadriceps muscle is tightened. The pain is worse on descending stairs and also after sitting. Although the X-ray is usually reported as normal it may show some thinning of the cartilage. Hyperextension of the knee joint above 10 degrees suggests hypermobility syndrome.

196:True 197:False 198:False 199:True 200:True 201:True
Practice annual reports must contain the numbers not the names of those patients who self refer themselves to casualty departments. Again the numbers not names of staff are required. The training undertaken by the staff needs to be recorded. All changes to the practice staff and buildings that have occurred during the last year and are planned for the next year need to be recorded. The numbers of people sent to all specialties needs to be included.

202:False 203:False 204:False 205:True 206:True
Delusions, although they occur in schizophrenia also occur in a wide variety of other psychiatric disorders. They cannot be altered by reason or demonstration of their falsity. An obsession is recognised by the person as

being illogical and often causes them distress. Delusions are often defined as morbid false beliefs and they are often secondary to hallucinations.

207:True 208:False 209:True 210:True 211:True
Hypothyroidism is missed at some time by most doctors! Symptoms are diverse and the doctor needs to be on his guard.

212:True 213:True 214:False 215:False
Opiate addicts have now become a problem for many GPs. Very few practitioners are licensed by the Home Office. For them methadone or some other opiates are suitable for maintenance treatment or withdrawal regimes. Methadone takes about 36 hours after the last dose before the symptoms of restlessness, insomnia and diarrhoea occur. A withdrawal regime can practically and humanely get an addict free of the drug within 2-4 weeks. Convulsions are more associated with sedative addiction withdrawal.

216:False 217:False 218:False 219:False 220:False
Requests for home births seem to be increasing. A GP is under no obligation to respond positively to these requests. A doctor need not be present at the delivery but a midwife must be. Abnormal deliveries are commoner in higher social classes and those who have had fetal monitoring. Only 6% of babies require any form of intervention after birth.

221:True 222:True 223:True 224:True 225:True
Any cause of upper airways obstruction can cause snoring e.g. retrognathic jaw, polyps, deviated septum. Hypothyroidism does because of tissue swelling.

One of the commonest presentations of obstructive sleep apnoea syndrome is excessive daytime sleepiness leading to falling asleep at meetings and whilst driving. Less common than the above symptoms are morning headaches and memory problems. If severe frequent oxygen desaturation leads to cardiovascular stress during the obstructive episodes this may be associated with systemic hypertension, cor pulmonale and cardiac arrhythmias.

226:False 227:True 228:True 229:False 230:True
Changing doctors was made much easier under the new contract. Once a patient has signed the registration form he is your responsibility. You have to offer a health check in writing and record the fact in the notes. Normally

a health check fee is paid for examinations done within 3 months of registration but the time limit can be extended if a satisfactory explanation is appended to the form. New patient examinations are an ideal time to catch up with immunisations and these attract an additional item of service payment unless they are routine childhood immunisations.

231:True 232:True 233:False 234:True 235:False
The drug is poorly absorbed if given concurrently with both magnesium and aluminium antacids. It has a broad spectrum of activity and is effective against pseudomonas. However it is less effective than doxycyline in chylamidial infections. If given to bronchitics it can cause potential serious theophylline toxicity because of microsomal enzyme inhibition.

236:False 237:True 238:True 239:False 240:True
In the last few years this has become the operation of choice for gall bladder disease in many centres. 90% of cases are suitable for laparoscopic surgery. Morbidity is low, day case surgery is common in America, patients are up and about on the day of surgery.

Operations take longer than conventional surgery. A nasogastric tube has to be passed to decompress the stomach to allow visualisation of the gall bladder.

241:False 242:True 243:True 244:False 245:True
The first feature to develop in pre-eclampsia is raised blood pressure, late features are proteinuria and a reversed circadian pattern of blood pressure, with it being elevated at night and lower in the day. Oedema is very common in pregnancy but in pre-eclampsia it is severe and generalised in the majority of women. There is no evidence that control of blood pressure arrests the progress of the disease.

246:False 247:False 248:True 249:False 250:False
Seborrhoeic eczema has a peak onset at 4-12 months, it usually involves the body, face, scalp and hands with erythema and scaliness but it is not itchy. It does resolve spontaneously in the vast majority of children. Emollients are the mainstay of treatment especially as soap substitutes. Atopic eczema involves the flexures, seborrhoeic does not.

251:False 252:True 253:True 254:False 255:True
Swelling of the cheek is virtually never caused by maxillary sinusitis, it would indicate an infection in the root of a tooth. Once the exit to the maxillary sinus is blocked the pain can become severe and can be felt in the teeth. In acute sinusitis the discharge becomes yellow or green and may be blood stained.

256:False 257:True 258:False 259:False 260:False
Health visitors usually have post basic training in midwifery and community nursing experience. Their statutory obligation is to continue visiting the baby once the midwife has stopped her visits, usually around the 10th day post delivery. They are attached staff employed by the health authority but fund holding practices are able to purchase their services directly after April 1993. Care of the elderly and over 75 visiting would seem to be a role suited to the skills and training of health visitors.

261:True 262:True 263:False 264:False 265:True
Chalazia are associated with blepharitis and acne rosacea. Blepharitis is commoner in people with eczema and psoriasis. Correction of an entropion is usually a minor procedure done under local anaesthetic.

Alkali is especially dangerous to the eye.

266:True 267:True 268:True 269:False 270:True
Drugs often produce changes in biochemical tests without producing any adverse effects on the patient. However, when an abnormal result is encountered it is important to know whether the patients medication could be held responsible before subjecting the patient to further investigations.

271:True 272:False 273:True 274:False 275:False
In the elderly it is ill health or death of a partner that stops people from having intercourse. Atrophic vaginitis itself is itchy and causes pain and soreness, secondary candida infection is common, but remember to exclude diabetes. The soreness induced by local oestrogens soon wears off with continued use.

276:True 277:True 278:True 279:False 280:False
Folic acid is found in liver, nuts and green vegetables. The daily requirement is 100-200 micrograms and it is absorbed in the duodenum and jejunum. Body stores last up to 4 months.

The macrocytosis induced by alcoholism is not folic acid dependent and in fact beer contains some folate.

281:True 282:True 283:True 284:True 285:False
Psychological problems have been shown to constitute one third of all consultations. Several surveys have shown that many of these problems are missed. Many factors within the patient and within the doctor either decrease or increase the number that are missed.

286:True 287:False 288:False 289:False 290:True
Absorbtion of drugs from the gut is influenced by many factors. If a drug is fat soluble the absorbtion will generally be enhanced in the presence of a fatty meal. Water soluble drugs such as digoxin and penicillin are best given with a drink of water one hour before a meal. The other three drugs in this question, are all gastric irritants and should be given with food.

291:True 292:True 293:True 294:False 295:True
All treatments for prostatic carcinoma whether surgical or medical seem to have the same prognosis. Current evidence suggests that microscopic asymptomatic disease is unlikely to spread within the patients lifetime and can be ignored. Stiboesterol alters blood coagulation and therefore increases cardiovascular mortality. Androgen receptor blockers are often given during the initial stages of treatment with gonadotrophin releasing analogues in order to prevent the exacerbation of bony pain associated with treatment at the onset of therapy with the latter.

296:True 297:True 298:False 299:True 300:True
With early discharge from hospital GPs are having to contend with more of the problems of jaundice in babies. So called 'physiological' jaundice starts at the 2nd day and peaks at the 4th day to disappear by the 10th day.

30-60% of all children will have discernible jaundice at some stage. Jaundice that persists or is intense should be investigated in a paediatric unit if possible. Infection and hypothyroidism are two of the most quoted causes for persisting jaundice.

301:True 302:False 303:True 304:False 305:True
Although the mean I.Q. is 80, it is often average or above. Specific learning difficulties are more common, but speech, language, hearing and visual

difficulties are rarely a problem. If a diplegia is present, the early development of spasticity is associated with a better outcome.

306:False 307:False 308:False 309:True 310:True
Reactive or stress polycythemia is a condition in which the red cell mass is normal but the PCV is raised, however rarely above 0.55. There are strong associations with male sex, smoking, alcoholism and obesity. Alcohol decreases plasma volume by inhibiting the release of anti-diuretic hormone. Obesity leads to hypoventilation and oxygen desaturation.

311:True 312:True 313:True 314:False 315:False
75% of couples will conceive within 12 months and a further 5% within the following year. The commonest reason for failure is tubal abnormality (20-30%) with disordered spermatogenesis next (15-20%) and then ovulation problems (10-15%). Reconstructive surgery is associated with at least a 25% chance of a full term pregnancy but an increased risk of ectopic pregnancy. Clomiphene induces ovulation in 70% of women previously anovulatory, however only half of these conceive. In-vitro techniques do not lead to an increase in the risk of abnormal babies.

316:True 317:False 318:True 319:False
Hyperventilation is typically associated with no history of relevant illness and absence of specific clinical findings. The peak expiratory flow rate is typically normal and there is no cyanosis. The overbreathing leads to a decrease in blood levels of carbon dioxide, producing alkalosis, this in turn leads to spontaneous discharge of peripheral nerves giving rise to paraesthesia, cramps and tetany.

320:False 321:True 322:True 323:False 324:False
The cost rent scheme is an extremely complex piece of legislation in which a practice may build new premises or substantially alter existing property. The interest on any loan is paid by the FHSA and the capital is paid by the partnership. The amount involved is generally independent of the district valuers assessment of the worth of the premises at the end of the project.

325:True 326:True 327:True
The classic studies of Murray Parkes showed that bereavement has a definite and high mortality for the remaining partner. Over 55 years of age the death rate for men is 40% in the first year following death of a spouse. Overall the

death rate is 20%. Even by the third year the death rate is still greater than for the normal population.

328:True 329:True 330:False 331:True 332:True
Unfavourable factors in depressive illness include an obsessional personality, previous significant depressive illness, loss of any parent but especially mother prior to the age of 12 years, bereavement in later life, no sympathetic close relationship, poor social circumstances, being housebound or tied to the house by an ill relative. Conversely, favourable factors include, a secure childhood, support from a friend or relative and an active social life with outside activities.

333:False 334:False 335:False 336:True 337:False
Progestogen only pills cause little or no change in clotting mechanisms and do not affect lipid levels. They need not be stopped prior to surgery. They are not secreted in breast milk. If started on the first day of the cycle they provide immediate protection. If started after a combined oral contraceptive has been given they should be commenced immediately after the last combined pill has been taken and not at the end of the 7 pill free days.

338:True 339:False 340:False 341:False
Under the Childrens Act the wishes of the child are paramount and the doctor must treat the child if he feels that the child is mature enough to make a decision about himself.

342:False 343:True 344:False 345:True
To claim PGEA 25 days of approved postgraduate education spread over the previous 5 years entitles a GP principal to make a claim for the full allowance. Unpaid clinical attachments under consultant supervision and distance learning courses can count. A recently trained GP principal must continue to attend 5 days of approved education per year after the first claim.

346:True 347:False 348:False 349:False 350:False
40% of throat swabs yield no growth, 30% are streptococcal, 20% viral and 10% other organisms including *Haemophilus*. The decrease in incidence of rheumatic fever and glomerulonephritis predates the introduction of antibiotics and is ascribed to the raised standards of cleanliness and housing conditions. Tonsillar exudate in an under 15 year old is more typical of streptococcus, in an over 15 year old of glandular fever. However the

appearances and the presence of lymphadenopathy are not characteristic of any specific type of infection.

351:False 352:True 353:True 354:False 355:False
The incidence of solar keratoses is increasing especially in fair skinned, fair haired people. About 10-25% of keratoses will develop into squamous cell carcinomas but it is usually a local tumour and they rarely metastasize. Basal cell carcinomas do metastasize but rarely (1:1000) and usually only to local lymph glands. Chronic sun exposure leads to loss of skin elasticity, an increase in telangiectasia and prominent sebaceous glands. Sunburn typically takes 4-8 hours to develop after exposure.

356:True 357:True 358:True 359:True 360:False
A study in the USA in 1980 showed that owning pets was associated with increased survival following myocardial infarction. An Australian study showed significant differences in blood pressure and lipid levels between pet owners and those without animals. A further study from Cambridge showed a 50% decrease in minor health problems within one month of cat or dog ownership. This reduction was maintained at 10 month follow up.

PAPER 5

1:False 2:False 3:False 4:True 5:False
Allergic conjunctivitis produces a discharge that is typically clear, mucopurulent discharge would indicate infection, visual acuity should not be affected and photophobia only occurs in very severe cases with involvement of the cornea. Epiphora and itching are the main symptoms. If the patient can tolerate contact lenses they are allowed.

6:True 7:False 8:False 9:True 10:False
Alcohol problems in women have increased over the last 20 years. Both cerebral and hepatic damage seems to be more prevalent in women. However, the incidence of cirrhosis has not yet reached the same level as for men. Women are far more likely to have an associated depressive illness than men. Alcohol intoxication is achieved with lower intake of alcohol during the premenstrual phase of the cycle. Women tend to start drinking

at a later age than men and consequently become problem drinkers at a later age also.

11:True 12:False 13:False 14:True 15:False
Controlled drug prescriptions must be handwritten by the prescriber. The address of the doctor is pre-printed on all prescriptions. The drug is marked C.D. in the BNF to denote that it is a controlled drug the prescription does not need to be marked with this.

16:True 17:True 18:False 19:True 20:True
Blood glucose levels have been shown to rise with age and 10% of the elderly are diabetic or have impaired glucose tolerance. Most people with glycosuria have diabetes but not all diabetics have glycosuria. Glucose tolerance testing is rarely needed and a raised fasting glucose is usually diagnostic.

Fluorescein angiography shows the presence of early retinal changes in the majority of diabetics.

21:True 22:True 23:True 24:False 25:True
Pain due to cervical arthritic change is typically worse at night. Carcinoma of the pyriform fossa causes pain in the ear via referred pain along the Xth cranial nerve. The upper molar teeth, temperomandibular joint or the parotid gland can all cause referred pain. Trigeminal neuralgia does not cause otalgia, but glossopharyngeal neuralgia can produce a severe lancinating pain in the ear or throat. Tonsillitis causes pain from the oropharynx via the IXth cranial nerve.

26:True 27:True 28:False 29:True 30:True
Chronic schizophrenia is characterised by the negative aspects of the illness with social withdrawal being pre-eminent. Depressive features are often marked with delusions, hallucinations and disordered thinking less prominent than in the acute stages of the illness. Complaints of physical symptoms are often the first evidence of schizophrenia.

31:True 32:False 33:True 34:True 35:False.
There are many different models of the consultation, one of the most practical and easy to remember is the one quoted in this question which is a more doctor centred approach. Four areas of the consultation are considered, the presenting problem, other problems, modifying health

seeking behaviour and finally prevention. The candidate is also advised to compare this with other models such as the one proposed by Pendleton et al.

36:True 37:True 38:True 39:True 40:True
The differential diagnosis of chest pain is fraught with problems. The symptoms given here are considered to point more to the functional nature of the chest pain.

41:True 42:True 43:False 44:False 45:False
Dermatofibromata are hard raised lesions which typically occur on the legs of young women, 20% of the female population develop one or more. They are usually brown and grow slowly over many years, the edges are smooth and they do not ulcerate. An irregular edge would indicate a malignant growth and if ulcerated this would be more in keeping with a pigmented rodent ulcer.

46:True 47:False 48:False 49:False 50:False
Immunisation with both types of hepatitis B vaccine is specific for that virus.

The preferred site of injection is the deltoid by deep IM route, injection into the buttocks may lead to depositing the vaccine in fatty tissue and the consequence of low absorbtion. The level of sero-conversion in children is virtually 100% with a decreased level in older patients. Systemic reactions are few with hypersensitivity being rare. Local reactions have been reported in 15% of vaccinations.

51:True 52:False 53:False 54:False 55:True 56:True
Psoriasis has a worldwide incidence of 2%. It does not scar and the lesions are rarely itchy. It can occur at any age but the peak incidence is in young adults. The rash is typically symmetrical, red and scaly with clearly defined borders. Although dithranol is the treatment of choice for plaque psoriasis it cannot be used on the face.

57:False 58:False 59:False 60:False 61:False
The care of epileptics still leaves a lot to be desired. All patients should be referred for assessment after their first fit. Idiopathic epilepsy is a dangerous diagnosis in those having a first convulsion after 25 years of age. Epilepsy is not an inherited condition in the majority of cases. Most GPs do not know

all their epileptic patients and they do not conduct annual checks on them as a matter of routine.

62:False 63:True 64:True 65:False 66:False
PACT data is automatically sent to all GPs at level 1. Level 3 is available on request and can be requested by individual therapeutic groups. The prescribing unit is based on the number of patients on the list with an additional allowance of 0.3 x the number of patients over 65 years of age, in order to compensate for increased prescribing in the elderly.

The Prescription Pricing Authority is alleged to have a high level of accuracy of the order of 99%.

Data is based on what the chemist dispenses, so if he has to split a pack, the PACT data will include the full pack price.

67:True 68:True 69:True 70:False 71:True
Listeria is present in soft cheeses, prepacked salads, salad creams and mayonnaise, uncooked and undercooked meats and poultry, pate, and unpasteurised milk.

Toxoplasma is excreted in cat faeces and anything that could be potentially contaminated by cats.

Exercise is to be encouraged, but care with starting exercise regimes in pregnancy should be taken if exercise was not undertaken in the pre-pregnant state.

72:True 73:True 74:True 75:False 76:False
A high index of suspicion is needed with anybody who has travelled further than Western Europe, especially if they have lived 'rough'.

Diarrhoeal illness must be thoroughly investigated, as for instance treating 'ulcerative colitis' with steroids can be fatal if it is really amoebiasis.

Lassa fever presents as a sore throat and fever, malaria with a non specific flu like illness in the early stages.

77:True 78:False 79:True 80:True 81:False
In one survey 1% of the population had suffered symptoms of post traumatic stress disorder. They occur soon after the event and can be helped by early expression of feelings with a professional care worker.

Individuals respond in different ways with a mixture of fears of annihilation, emotional problems and reactions provoked by a challenge to control. About 20-25% of those involved in a major disaster go on to develop a chronic disorder.

82:False 83:True 84:False 85:True 86:False
Episcleritis is usually a localised area of inflammation and is a self limiting condition. Visual disorder in ophthalmic herpes may indicate corneal scarring. Corneal ulcers need referral or sight may be lost. Corneal abrasions are usually dealt with in general practice. Blocked tear ducts in children can be left until 9 months of age and referral then is not urgent.

87:True 88:True 89:True 90:False 91:True
Reye's syndrome is rare but important as early diagnosis and treatment improves prognosis. It is associated with a previous infection which is probably showing signs of resolution. Vomiting is typically profuse and the child becomes overactive, combative and irritable before becoming lethargic and then comatose with signs of cerebral irritation. Liver function is always disturbed although jaundice is rare.

The peak incidence is 2 years. The association with aspirin ingestion has led to a decrease in the paediatric use of this drug and a consequential fall in incidence of the syndrome.

92:False 93:True 94:False 95:True 96:True
Only 15% of GPs have direct access to community hospitals. The average age of patients within these hospitals has risen because of a decrease in maternity work. Care is cheaper in community hospitals. The workload of doctors in these hospitals is greater but so is the job satisfaction.

97:True 98:False 99:True 100:True 101:True
Propranolol and nifedipine both have negative inotropic actions and therefore may precipitate heart failure. The hypoglycaemic effect of glibenclamide is antagonised by thiazide diuretics. Spironolactone is a potassium conserving diuretic and frusemide causes loss of potassium from

the body. NSAIDs all reduce platelet adhesiveness and potentiate the anticoagulation achieved with warfarin. Alcohol and antihistamines are both CNS depressants.

102:True 103:False 104:True 105:True 106:False
Now replacing hysterectomy in many centres, this procedure is suitable for most patients except for those with malignant or premalignant conditions of the endometrium or those with active pelvic infection. The endometrium needs to be thinned pre-operatively with danazol. Day case surgery is increasing and at the most it requires an overnight stay. The ideal result is to cause complete amenorrhoea but a scanty loss is deemed acceptable.

107:True 108:True 109:True 110:False 111:False
Achilles tendon problems are a common source of injuries in sports enthusiasts. Common factors precipitating tendonitis are a high heel tab, a low heel, running on a hard surface or a sudden change of running surface. Local steroid injections are traditionally associated with an increased incidence of rupture. Rupture is best treated by repair then immobilisation. Tendonitis is best treated initially by a heel raise and ultrasound combined with rest from the precipitating activity.

112:False 113:False 114:True 115:False 116:False
HIV positive patients run a variable period before symptoms of the disease manifest themselves. The earliest sign is generalised lymphadenopathy which heralds the commencement of AIDS related complex. This may produce weight loss, night sweats. diarrhoea and fatigue. The diagnosis of AIDS proper depends upon the presence of opportunistic infection or neoplasm such as non Hodgkin's lymphoma, Kaposi's sarcoma or *Pneumocystis* infection.

117:False 118:False 119:True 120:True 121:True
Innocent murmurs are typically systolic, sitting or deep inspiration makes an innocent murmur quieter. An innocent murmur is soft and there is no thrill, the ECG and CXR are normal.

122:False 123:True 124:False 125:True 126:False
Mania is characterised by elevated mood, increased activity and self important ideas, insight is lost. It is associated with episodes of profound depression which make the consequences of previous hypomanic behaviour even more difficult to live with.

127:True 128:False 129:False 130:False 131:True
Exposure to asbestos leads to an increase in lung cancer in both non smokers and smokers, asbestosis does not have to be present. Compounds formed in the manufacture of aniline dyes are associated with bladder cancer. Exposure to radon gas in miners was the first described occupational association with lung cancer.

132:True 133:True 134:True 135:False 136:True
Tinnitus is often the first symptom of Menieres disease and may occur episodically long before the first full attack. The feeling of fullness in the ear often accompanies tinnitus in the acute attack and may become intense. Hearing tends to decrease with each attack. Nystagmus only occurs during the acute attack. If Rombergism is present it would indicate either other pathology or an emotional overlay.

137:False 138:False 139:True 140:True 141:True
Splenomegaly occurs in glandular fever but the spleen is soft and friable and not easily palpable. Carcinomatosis rarely causes an enlarged spleen, a nodular, enlarged liver is a more common finding. Massive splenomegaly is most commonly due to chronic myeloid leukaemia or myelofibrosis.

142:False 143:False 144:True 145:True 146:True
Consent of the husband or father of the baby is not required prior to a therapeutic termination of pregnancy. If the mother is under 16 years of age, the consent of her parents is not necessarily required, however, the doctor would be well advised to consult the medical defence organisation. Form HSA2 is for emergency situations where only one doctor is available. Form HSA3 is for notification that an operation has taken place and is sent to the Department of Health.

147:False 148:False 149:True 150:True 151:False
As from April 1993 health promotion banding payments are calculated on 3 levels:

> Band 1 concentrates on the detection of people who smoke.
> Band 2 on minimising mortality from hypertension, coronary artery disease and stroke.
> Band 3 on reducing the incidence of coronary artery disease and stroke by primary intervention programmes.

Payments are based on the average list size of a general practitioner in England and Wales. Diabetic and asthma clinics are recipients of an additional small payment.

Pre-existing clinics are not paid but transitional payments are available for practices which will lose a substantial amount of their remuneration.

152:True 153:True 154:True 155:True 156:True
Anticoagulant therapy monitoring can suddenly produce results that fluctuate from an apparently stable situation. Often no reason can be found however it is worth reviewing the intercurrent medication and if necessary looking for signs and symptoms of illness.

157:True 158:True 159:True 160:True 161:True
Smoking has an immunosuppressant effect and decreases the immune response. Therefore diseases such as farmer's lung and ulcerative colitis are reduced. Nicotine may affect dopaminergic activity in the brain and therefore the incidence of Parkinson's disease and Alzheimer's disease is reduced. Smoking reduces the incidence of circulating oestrogen levels and there is a lower incidence of dysmenorrhoea, uterine fibroids and endometriosis.

162:False 163:False 164:True 165:True 166:True
The incidence of carcinoma of the oesophagus is rising, possibly due to the increased ingestion of nitrosamines and alcohol. The prognosis is poor and especially worse for adenocarcinoma. The commonest presenting symptoms are dysphagia for solids only and weight loss.

167:True 168:False 169:True 170:True
Psychological factors are of great importance in the management of chronic pain. It is important that the general practitioner appreciates that fear, anxiety and social and physical isolation increase the perception of pain. Also the patients personality type affects the overall comprehension of the pain. Placebo affects are great and this needs to be taken into account when gauging the response to therapy.

171:True 172:True 173:False 174:True 175:True
Beta-sympathomimetics, anticholinergic and sodium cromoglycate all have proven efficacy when given via a nebuliser. Beclomethazone is available but efficacy is not proven. Theophyllines are oral or injectable preparations.

176:True 177:True 178:False 179:False 180:True
Diverticular disease is common and often asymptomatic. Rectal bleeding is a frequent presentation and does not usually indicate underlying malignancy. The best treatment is non fermentable fibre of which coarse wheat bran is the most effective. Fistula can occur and may cause pneumaturia if connecting with the bladder.

181:False 182:False 183:True 184:False 185:False
There is a 'pecking' order of relatives from husband or wife down to nephews and nieces. The majority of admissions are under Section 2. Section 4 should rarely be used except for extreme emergencies. Only a relative or an approved social worker can make an application for admission. Sexual deviancy, alcoholism and drug abuse are not in themselves grounds for admission.

Section 139 protects doctors employing the act from legal retribution if they are over enthusiastic.

186:False 187:False 188:False 189:False 190:False
There is no relationship between the tolerance to adverse and to therapeutic effects. Tolerance may develop in less than 48 hours after the initiation of treatment, but is rapidly abolished once there is a nitrate free period. There is no difference between the various preparations quoted in the question, what is important is the length of time above the therapeutic level likely to cause tolerance in any one particular patient.

191:False 192:False 193:False 194:True 195:True
Testicular torsion has a peak incidence between 12-18 years, not epididymitis. Iliac fossa pain is again typical of testicular torsion. In epididymitis the scrotal contents rapidly swell due to enlargement of epididymal structures. High frequency B mode ultrasound is able to differentiate between torsion and epididymitis. Chlamydial infection is associated with non-specific urethritis.

196:True 197:False 198:True 199:True 200:True
The causes of agitation in the elderly are legion. The GP should be wary of all drug therapy especially if recently introduced but also if used for many years. Depressive illness may be the cause of agitation and it could be worsened by benzodiazepines. Silent infarcts are common and vigilance is

needed if they are to be detected. A withdrawn patient may not drink and in warm weather can soon become dehydrated leading to agitation.

201:True 202:True 203:False 204:False 205:True
'Frozen shoulder' is a generic term encompassing a variety of conditions which are not always clinically distinguishable. It usually runs a chronic course of about 2 years then recovers completely. Local tenderness over the various muscles e.g. supraspinatus, infraspinatus or biceps tendon reflects the site of the lesion accurately. Immobilisation may lead to permanent restriction of movement and exercise should be encouraged. The condition may be precipitated by unusual exertion such as home decorating and the pain is often worse at night.

206:False 207:True 208:True 209:True 210:False
In the UK sarcoid is the commonest cause of hilar lymphadenopathy in patients over 15 years of age. In lymphoma the glands may be mediastinal rather than hilar. Hilar glands due to tubercle are commoner in children but the incidence is increasing in adults especially in large cities.

211:False 212:False 213:True 214:False 215:False
Atypia is often due to human papilloma virus, however a single abnormal smear does not correlate well with the presence of CIN. However, if 2 or 3 smears show atypia, colposcopy should be performed. If there is evidence of genital warts a smear should be taken annually until negative smears have occurred on 5 successive occasions. Cervical erosions may bleed on touch during taking the smear but they do not show any typical abnormality.

Carcinoma of the cervix is usually diagnosed on clinical history and appearance of the cervix.

216:True 217:False 218:False 219:False 220:True
Irritant contact dermatitis as contrasted with allergic contact dermatitis does not require the patient to have been exposed previously. The rash typically develops within 24 hours as opposed to 2-4 days for allergy. The severity of the rash depends on the amount of irritant used whereas in allergic conjunctivitis only a small quantity can produce a severe reaction. Reactivation at other sites does not occur in irritant conjunctivitis.

221:True 222:True 223:True 224:False 225:False
With prolonged use it is possible to develop anti-calcitonin antibodies. Pagetic bone is highly vascular and a 'steal' syndrome can occur leading to high output cardiac failure. Bone overgrowth can lead to deafness when foramina in the skull close. 10% of patients with the disease will have a normal alkaline phosphatase prior to the commencement of treatment.

226:True 227:False 228:True 229:True 230:True
Toddler diarrhoea is common, the child passes several loose stools per day with undigested food (typically carrots and peas) in the stools. There is never failure to thrive unless other pathology is present. If it occurs, further investigation is necessary.

Sometimes, it occurs after an acute infective illness and especially in these patients a milk free diet is helpful. Loperamide is of some use in cases which are proving to be intractable and in which there is no other cause.

231:False 232:True 233:True 234:False 235:True
Only about one third of patients on benzodiazepines will become dependent on their drug. The first sign of dependency is often rebound sleep disturbance which has been shown to occur after one week in some people. The loss of appetite which occurs can often be severe enough to cause weight loss. More severe symptoms include auditory and visual hallucinations. Beta-blockers have been shown to help but not every patient who is having problems with stopping their drugs.

236:False 237:False 238:False 239:False 240:True
Scientific and medical papers quote a lot of statistics and it is a good idea to have a rudimentary knowledge of some of the concepts. The Null hypothesis is concerned with results that could occur by chance. The Student's 't' test is of use in small groups of data. Spearman's rank correlation is used when comparing rank correlated groups of data.

241:False 242:True 243:False 244:True 245:False
The cap, contraceptive diaphragm, should be left in situ for 6 hours after intercourse to be truly effective. Variations in size of the patient can make it ineffective because of poor fitting, similarly if a prolapse is present the seal will not be adequate. The frequency of replacement depends upon usage, however they should be changed annually because the rubber may perish. All available caps quoted in the drug tariff are made from rubber.

246:True 247:False 248:True 249:True 250:False
Hyoscine (Scopaderm) is available as a transdermal patch, the effect of which lasts for 72 hours. Domperidone is available as syrup, tablets and suppositories, the injection was withdrawn because of an association with cardiac arrhthymias. Cinnarazine (Stugeron) is available over the counter from the pharmacist and is effective for travel sickness. Procloperazine is associated with parkinsonian side effects, hypotension and occasionally acute dystonic reactions. Finally, chlorpromazine has a very weak anti-emetic effect and should not be used for this purpose.

251:True 252:False 253:False 254:True 255:True
Febrile convulsions typically occur between 6 months and 6 years of age. There is no social class difference and there is no difference in the sex incidence. Prolonged fits are associated with residual neurological deficit. There is a 15% chance of a child having febrile convulsions if a first degree relative has had them. In the normal population the risk is quoted as 7%.

256:True 257:False 258:False 259:False 260:False
Sclerotherapy gives good short term results but high saphenous ligation with multiple avulsions is the mainstay of treatment. After treatment, compression is only needed for about one week and walking should commence on the day of surgery. The majority of patients only need one week away from work.

261:True 262:False 263:False 264:False 265:True
In pregnancy about one third of patients will show an increase in fit frequency. 70% of those with migraine have been shown to improve. Multiple sclerosis is rarely affected by the pregnancy but relapses are common in the puerperium. Asthma appears to be unaffected. Sickle cell disease has a high mortality and needs skilled management.

266:True 267:False 268:True 269:False 270:True
Before replacing soft lenses in an eye which has been stained with fluorsecein it must be thoroughly irrigated with saline. Pilocarpine characteristically causes tight constriction of the pupils. Benoxinate is a local anaesthetic, tropicamide is a short acting drug which dilates the pupils and is useful in diabetic clinics. The local irritation caused by adrenaline is avoided by giving it as a pro-drug.

271:True 272:False 273:False 274:True 275:True
The syndrome of acute inflammatory polyneuropathy is an acute peripheral demyelinating condition which has a rapid onset. Motor symptoms predominate and paralysis may be profound requiring assisted ventilation. The majority of cases make a satisfactory recovery and usually remain free of problems.

276:True 277:True 278:True 279:True 280:True
Good control of diabetes preconceptually and during the first trimester will decrease the incidence of congenital abnormalities. Pre-term labour is commoner and babies born early are at a greater risk of Respiratory Distress Syndrome than babies of equivalent gestation born to non diabetic mothers.

There is an unexplained incidence of fetal death after 40 weeks gestation and pregnancies are usually induced no later than term.

281:True 282:True 283:False 284:True 285:True
Tuberculosis is possible but is more common at a younger age. Perthes' disease has a peak incidence between 6-8 years and is more common in boys than girls. Slipped upper femoral epiphysis is typically pre-pubertal. Septic arthritis would be accompanied by pyrexia and malaise. Non-accidental injury is possible but is commoner in the under 3 year old.

286:False 287:False 288:True 289:False 290:True
With erythema multiforme, there is usually a precipitating cause either a viral infection, bacterial infection or drug eruption. The rash is characteristic with round papules or blisters made up of rings of different colours (Target or Iris lesions.) If mucous membranes are involved this is known as the Steven's-Johnson syndrome and carries a significant mortality. Recurrent episode are common especially if it follows a Herpes simplex infection.

291:True 292:False 293:True 294:False 295:False
The MRFIT study in North America established that cholesterol was a risk factor and other studies have shown that decreasing serum cholesterol by 10% decreases cardiovascular mortality. However, no study has shown a decrease in overall mortality. One study showed that a very low cholesterol was associated with an increased risk of malignancy especially carcinoma of the colon.

Good dietary control following counselling will decrease the level of cholesterol on average by 10-15%. The various risk factors are additive and therefore people who smoke and/or have a raised blood pressure are probably more in need of screening.

296:True 297:True 298:True 299:False 300:False
Low dose aspirin is now very widely prescribed but it is not without side effects both in the short term or the long term. After a myocardial infarction studies have shown a significant decrease in long term mortality if given at a dose of 150 mg for one month. In the treatment of venous thrombosis it does not appear to have a role, however it may have a place in prevention of thrombosis. It has no role in the primary prevention of cerebrovascular disease and may even increase the risk of cerebral haemorrhage.

301:False 302:True 303:True 304:True
The diagnosis of child abuse is fraught with difficulties, however there are certain pointers, such as an implausible explanation for the injuries, previous abuse or abuse in siblings. The children are usually less than 3 years of age (contrasting with sexual abuse which may well continue into adolescence.)

305:True 306:True 307:False 308:True 309:True
Baldness is usually physiological, however it may be associated with local disease of the scalp such as seborrhoeic eczema, tinea capitis, or simply hair pulling (trichotillomania). Minoxidil topically applied twice daily is effective in some people in treating male pattern baldness. However, hair regrowth stops and reverses within 3 months of cessation of therapy. Endocrine causes such as pituitary or adrenal tumours can cause hirsutism and hair loss. Hormone replacement treatment is associated with excessive hair loss in some patients.

310:False 311:False 312:True 313:False
Stress and urgency incontinence require different treatments and are often confused. Stress incontinence is typically associated with leaking of urine on coughing sneezing or laughter, leaking on playing sport or sudden movement. Urgency incontinence or detrusor instability is more likely with a history of frequency of 6 or more times per day and 3 or more times at night, leaking at night and having to rush to the toilet. Dribbling is a symptom of overflow incontinence.

314:True 315:False 316:False
The statement of fees and allowances are negotiated by the GMSC and government, there needs to be no legislative change to amend these under the NHS regulations.

317:False 318:False 319:True 320:True
This allowance replaces and extends the benefits that were previously available as the attendance allowance and the mobility allowance. The disability should have arisen prior to the age of 65 years of age. It is paid after a qualifying period of 3 months (the attendance allowance previously was 6 months). It is a tax free allowance and is not means tested.

321:False 322:False 323:False 324:False
There is no evidence that restriction of tea, coffee or cola decreases symptoms of p.m.s. An hourly starch diet may relieve symptoms in some patients. Fertility is not affected. About 20-40% of women consult their doctor at least once with symptoms of the condition. Approximately 150 different symptoms have been attributed to p.m.s. Suppression of ovulation by using either high dose oestrogen patches or the oral contraceptive does give a small reduction in symptoms in some patients but conversely some women report a worsening of symptoms.

325:False 326:False 327:True 328:False 329:False
The most likely effect of most of these is one of mild gastrointestinal upset. If in doubt always check with the local poisons information centre.

330:False 331:True 332:True 333:True 334:False 335:False
Grapefruit contains 0.5g of fibre per 100g, banana has 6 times this amount. Spinach is always quoted as a good source of iron, it has 4mg/100g and corn flakes 7mg/100g. People on diets often stop eating bread and eat crispbread instead, 100g of rye crispbread has 320 kcal, the equivalent of wholemeal bread 220 kcal.

Green peppers are very rich in vitamin C with 100mg/100g (compare with oranges 40mg/100g). There is no significant difference between red and white wines each has between 65-70 kcal/100g. Beer contains a small amount of niacin (0.3mg/100g) but no other vitamins of the B complex.

336:True 337:True 338:True 339:True 340:False
Carbon monoxide poisoning accounts for about 1000 deaths per year in England and Wales. Faulty appliances and blocked vents are the usual cause. The initial symptom is often a dull pounding headache very like a hangover, mental apathy, nausea, and dizziness are also typical symptoms. If the exposure continues, convulsions, coma and respiratory distress follow. The skin typically becomes pink and cyanosis does not occur.

The toxic effects are usually reversed within 12 hours of removal from the source of the carbon monoxide.

341:False 342:True 343:False 344:False 345:False
Azoospermia or oligospermia can be caused by the inadvertent use of spermicides but once simple causes have been excluded little hope can be given that a treatable cause will be found. If FSH levels are raised in a patient with small firm testicles further investigation is necessary especially to exclude a chromosomal abnormality such as Klinefelter's syndrome.

By careful investigation a cause for the condition can be identified in about two thirds of cases but only in a very few cases can a treatment be instituted which will lead to a successful outcome.

346:True 347:True 348:False 349:True 350:False
Oral decongestants are taken usually as over the counter remedies and may contain one or all of the following, paracetamol, phenylpropanolamine, phenylephrine, pseudoephedrine, antihistamine. They need to be used with caution in a variety of conditions. They can induce a hypertensive crisis especially in people taking non selective beta blockers. They stimulate the heart and cause an increase in oxygen demand and therefore should not be used in patients with ischaemic heart disease and hypertension. They can induce arrhythmias especially in hyperthyroidism and can induce a rise in blood glucose and should not be used in diabetics.

351:True 352:False 353:False 354:True 355:False
In 1992 notifications increased for the first time for many years, however there is still a significant under reporting of the disease which has been estimated as about 25%. In the USA new cases have increased dramatically.

Drug resistant strains do occur but 95% of isolates are sensitive to all standard drugs (isoniazid, rifampicin, ethambutol, and streptomycin).

Although trials in some parts of the world have shown BCG to be ineffective, in Britain there is overwhelming evidence for its efficacy.

The homeless are significantly at risk as are patients with AIDS, however in Britain the number of such patients developing tuberculosis is approximately 5%.

356:True 357:True 358:True 359:False 360:True
In Britain and Scandinavia chronic low blood pressure has been dismissed as of no consequence. Conversely in the continental countries, especially France and Germany, it is often treated more seriously than raised blood pressure. Studies, some published in the BMJ have highlighted the fact that patients with the condition do have a significant morbidity and a perceived feeling of being unwell. The studies do not show if elevation of the blood pressure causes the symptoms described to disappear.

PasTest Books and Intensive Revision Courses

MRCGP Practice Exams: Second Edition

John Sandars RCGP Examiner
Rebecca Baron Vocational Course Organiser

Written by a Royal College Examiner, the book is a practical guide to passing the MRCGP examination. It contains 360 MCQs in the new format, 2 complete MEQ papers, Critical Reading Question papers with two published papers and a structured approach to critical reading. Answers, marking schedules and teaching notes are included together with advice on the Oral examinations. A guide to revision planning, a revision checklist and recommended reading list are also included. No candidate should be without this book. *ISBN: 0 906986 92 4*

MRCGP WEEKEND COURSES (London and Manchester)

These high quality professional courses are run by RCGP examiners and are designed to cover all aspects of the exam: MCQs, MEQs, Critical Reasoning, revision planning, popular topics, oral videos, working papers, analyses and discussion. Past College exam questions form the basis for all teaching sessions. Practice questions are forwarded for completion before the course. These courses are approved under Section 63 and PGEA, and are held in April and October each year.

PasTest Books and Intensive Revision Courses for the **DCH** and **DRCOG** examinations are also available.

REQUEST FORM

Please send me by return of post the information ticked below:

List of PasTest Revision Books   ☐
MRCGP courses: London ☐   Manchester ☐
DCH courses: London ☐   Manchester ☐
DRCOG courses: London ☐   Manchester ☐

Name _____

Address _____

_____

Telephone _____

Please post this form to:
     PasTest, Rankin House, Parkgate Estate, Knutsford
     Cheshire WA16 8DX. Tel 0565 755226 Fax 0565 650264

GPN